ENVIRONMENTAL POLLUTION BY CHEMICALS

COLIN WALKER

Department of Physiology and Biochemistry
University of Reading

HUTCHINSON EDUCATIONAL

HUTCHINSON EDUCATIONAL LTD
3 Fitzroy Square, London W1

London Melbourne Sydney Auckland
Wellington Johannesburg Cape Town
and agencies throughout the world

First published 1971

*This book has been set in Times type, printed in Great Britain
on smooth wove paper by Anchor Press, and
bound by Wm. Brendon, both of Tiptree, Essex*

ISBN 0 09 107991 8

Contents

Acknowledgements

I would like to thank the following for permission to reproduce illustrations that appear in the text: Dr K. Mellanby and Mr I. Prestt of the Nature Conservancy (Figures 5.7 and 5.6), Dr J. Robinson of Shell Research Ltd (Figure 5.4) and the Laboratory of the Government Chemist (Figure 6.4).

I am also grateful to Professor K. Simkiss for his interest and helpful advice.

C.W.

Reading, 1971

Illustrations

Preface

Used in its broadest sense, the term 'pollution' refers to any change in the natural quality of the environment brought about by chemical, physical or biological factors. Since the pristine state of the environment is hard to define, it is not always clear where the word should be applied. Should changes brought about by wildlife or volcanic action be regarded as pollutions, for example? In practice, 'pollution' nearly always refers to the consequences of human activity, and this is the sense in which it will be used here.

Pollutions arising from changes of temperature and other physical factors or from bacterial contamination do not fall within the scope of this book. Neither do those caused by smoke, dust, grit, sewage particles or other chemically heterogeneous materials except in so far as they may contain particular polluting substances (pollutants). Thus smoke, for example, is only discussed in connection with the polycyclic aromatic hydrocarbons that it contains.

This account is limited to pollutants that are found in the environment at large. Individuals have little opportunity of avoiding exposure to most of them, short of taking up residence in remote areas of the world. Clearly, most drugs and food additives, together with those industrial poisons which present purely occupational hazards, do not fall within these terms of reference. At the same time most drugs, like most pollutants, are foreign compounds to living animals. Much of our present knowledge of the processes involved in the elimination of such substances from the body is based upon work with drugs. Thus it will be necessary to make some reference to them in connection with elimination of pollutants by animals.

It is not the purpose of this book to give a comprehensive account of all chemical pollutants. Examples have been selected which are fairly well documented and which illustrate important principles. It should not be assumed, however, that the substances most widely investigated are those which present most risk. In the first place, studies on pollution are usually undertaken in response to changes that are readily observed. Since very little is known about chemical pollution many effects have probably passed unnoticed and have therefore not been considered for study. Again, the amount of work that is done on a recognised pollutant is not simply related to the apparent risk. The way the subject is treated by the mass media can be highly

9

influential with regard to both public reaction and official policy.

One important and widely studied group of pollutants has been excluded – the radioactive ions formed during nuclear reactions. These substances present special problems, and it was felt that a satisfactory treatment was not possible within the scope of this book.

Some pollutants cause particular concern because they are described as poisons; but it is important to remember that this term only gives a rough indication of relative toxicity. Even such 'non-poisonous' substances as glucose and common salt can be injurious or lethal when they are present at sufficiently high concentrations in living organisms. By the same token, familiar poisons such as carbon monoxide and arsenious oxide are apparently harmless at relatively low concentrations. Indeed, the ingestion of small quantities of arsenious oxide has been claimed by some mountaineers to be beneficial on the grounds that it improves 'wind'. Terms such as 'moderately toxic' and 'highly toxic' are useful for giving more precise information about particular poisons. In practice, 'poisonous' pollutants in the living environment are usually present at levels well below those known to have harmful effects, a point to be borne in mind when reading popular articles on this subject.

Much of the concern about chemical pollution centres on possible harmful effects upon man and beneficial organisms. For this reason, a chapter has been devoted to the interaction of foreign compounds with living organisms. The question of the metabolism, distribution, excretion and mode of action of pollutants underlies such problems as persistence, accumulation along food chains, selective toxicity and sub-lethal effects.

To emphasise the relationship between physico-chemical properties and pollution problems, the pollutants discussed here are arranged into four groups, each represented by a separate chapter. The groups are: gases; heavy metals; liposoluble insecticides and fungicides; detergents, polycyclic aromatic hydrocarbons and polychlorinated biphenyls. The first group demonstrate the pollution problems associated with the gaseous state, and the heavy metals discussed here are all represented by ions which can interact with organic substances. The insecticides and fungicides illustrate the problems connected with pronounced fat solubility, whilst the final group of organic substances display contrasts in properties which are reflected in their behaviour in the environment.

The final chapter deals with assessment of risks and control of pollution and includes a discussion of the legal, political, economic and aesthetic factors involved. For pollution is truly an interdisciplinary problem. It provides an example of the way in which scientists from many disciplines, together with politicians, administrators and journalists, may be involved in a common problem of concern to the community as a whole.

Since some of the terms introduced in these chapters may be unfamiliar to the general reader, a glossary has been provided at the end of the book.

I

Pollution of the Gross Environment

MAN, like other animals, is affected by, and has effects upon, the environment in which he lives. He has brought about great changes in the natural environment both intentionally and accidentally, sometimes with disastrous consequences. The Kansas dust bowl of the 1930's and the London smog of 1952 are two familiar cases.

Man affects his environment by farming the land, by removing fish from the rivers and oceans, by building cities, and in many other ways. Chemical pollution should be seen against this background; as one factor amongst many others. Although man has released chemicals into the environment since early times, it is particularly a problem of the present day; an inevitable accompaniment of technological advance and increasing population density.

Pollution raises many questions about possible effects upon life which will be discussed in later chapters of this book. Before doing so, however, it is necessary to take account of the entry, distribution and persistence of pollutants with respect to the environment at large.

The gross environment may be divided into the air, the land surface, and the surface waters. Of these, the air is the most continuous, maintaining a connection between the land and the rivers, lakes and oceans. Owing to this and to its mobility, local atmospheric contamination may lead to world-wide pollution of air, land and sea. When the island of Krakatoa was shattered by a volcanic eruption in 1883, some of the dust reached the higher levels of the atmosphere and encircled the world, causing vividly coloured sunsets during the following months. More recently, man-made pollutants such as radioactive strontium and iodine have provided further evidence of the long-range dispersal of materials by the atmosphere. In the U.S.A., dust storms in Texas have caused dust-borne pesticides to travel as far afield as Georgia in the air currents. On an even wider scale, small residues of DDT have been detected in polar ice, brought down by snow after travelling very large distances in the air. Thus aerial dispersal ensures that pollution is an international problem.

There are many ways in which the atmosphere may become polluted. In early times the burning of fuels and the smelting of ores released carbon dioxide and other gases into the air. As early as the thirteenth century coal fires were causing winter fog in cities. Following the Industrial Revolution the 'dark satanic mills' and the steam engine added their contributions, to be followed in the twentieth century by the internal combustion engine and the nuclear bomb.

Air pollution is most serious in towns, especially in industrial towns that do not have smoke-free zones. That it can have serious, even fatal consequences has been well established. What is less certain is the relative importance of different sources of air pollution. At the present time the pattern of pollution is changing in Britain. Although we are now seeing tighter control of emissions from fires and furnaces, vehicles driven by petrol continue to go from strength to strength, making an increasing contribution to pollution in most urban areas. Furthermore, the rapid growth of air transport is increasing pollution by aero engines.

Atmospheric pollutants may exist as gases or as suspended particles or droplets. They vary greatly in their stability in air and reaction products are sometimes more troublesome than the original compounds. The Los Angeles 'smog' provides an example of this. Organic materials and oxides of nitrogen are released by car exhausts, and they interact under the influence of sunlight to form peroxyacetyl nitrate and other noxious substances.

Pollution of water does not appear to have been a serious problem until relatively recently. With high-density settlement in towns and cities came the question of sewage disposal, which had not troubled more dispersed communities. Excrement had undoubtedly entered rivers and streams in earlier times, but only in small quantities. With the growth of industry rivers and oceans provided a means of dispersing waste products from industrial processes. Nowadays, effluents from factories, waste materials dumped by ocean-going vessels, pesticides from agricultural land and washings from old mine workings all cause pollution of surface waters.

Water may be polluted by substances that dissolve in it, and by solid particles and liquid droplets which become suspended in it. Whereas true solutes tend to be distributed fairly uniformly throughout the medium, this is not true of insoluble substances. Sometimes there are serious consequences of this unequal distribution. When immiscible liquids such as oils enter waters they form surface films if they are less dense than the medium. An obvious effect of pollution of this kind is oiling of sea-birds which is often a cause of high mortality. Less apparent are indirect effects such as the limitation of oxygen uptake by water when it is covered by a film of oil. This can lead to serious oxygen shortage and consequently to high mortality in fish and other aquatic organisms. Insoluble solids also tend to have an irregular distribution in water. They usually concentrate at the water surface and/or in the bottom sediment rather than in the main body of water. Insoluble insecticides such as DDT and dieldrin are marketed as solutions in oily liquids (emulsifiable concentrates). When these preparations get into water, the oil tends to float on the water surface with the insecticides dissolved in it.

Many pollutants entering water do not constitute a problem because they are broken down or immobilised. Disregarding metabolic breakdown which is dealt with in the next chapter, there are purely chemical processes that tend to limit pollution problems. A number of toxic organic compounds are unstable in water and are quickly broken down into inactive substances. The organophosphorus insecticide T.E.P.P., for example, is readily hydrolysed by water and the products of hydrolysis are inactive. Ordinary soaps interact with calcium, magnesium and other ions present in natural waters to produce insoluble salts which float on the surface as a scum. This process, which occurs most readily in hard waters rich in calcium and magnesium, minimises the tendency of the soap to lower surface tension, i.e. it reduces the chances of the soap causing foaming.

Some Welsh rivers are heavily polluted with lead washed from disused mine workings. The element occurs mainly in the form of Pb^{2+} ion, and steps are being taken to reduce its concentration in affected waters. Some success has been achieved by passing mine effluents through limestone beds to remove lead.

Considering long-term pollution of surface waters, it is lakes and seas rather than rivers that give the greatest cause for concern. Although cases of river pollution (e.g. the kill of Rhine fish in 1969 caused by endosulfan) have sometimes been dramatic, they have generally been reversible. River systems are to some extent self-cleansing, washing persistent substances from their courses into lakes and oceans. Where river pollution is traceable to a definite point of entry (outfall) rather than general run-off or seepage from the land, there is a steady dilution of pollutant with movement downstream. That is to say, a concentration gradient exists where the concentration falls off with increasing distance downstream from the outfall. If pollution occurs fairly continuously, a biological sequence can be established as a result of it. Only the least susceptible species are found nearest the outfall, with more susceptible species reappearing further downstream with decreasing concentration of pollutant (Figure 1.1).

All this contrasts with the situation in lakes and seas where there is a real risk of long-term build-up of persistent compounds as they are steadily brought in by rivers. Already there are ominous signs. The Baltic Sea has yielded fish with such high levels of DDT and related compounds that the Swedish authorities have pronounced them unfit for human consumption. Loch Leven in Scotland has become highly polluted and this has caused changes in the flora and fauna. Again there is the mysterious case of high concentrations of polychlorinated biphenyls in sea-birds from the Irish Sea where the source of pollution has not yet been identified (see Chapter VI). The oceans are bridges between continents, and the movement of pollutants in ocean currents underlines the point that pollution is an international problem.

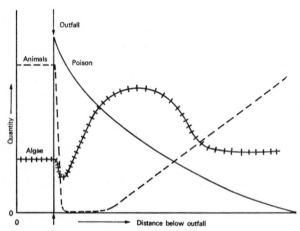

Fig. 1.1 Diagrammatic representation of the effects of a poisonous effluent on a river (After H. B. N. Hynes *The Biology of Polluted Waters*)

Despite the rapid growth of towns and new road developments, soils still account for a high proportion of the land surface. They are included here as part of the gross environment for reasons of convenience although they are really complex associations of living organisms and inorganic material. In contrast to their behaviour in air and surface waters, pollutants do not move readily once they are in the soil unless they are gases, in which case they diffuse through the air channels. Thus many compounds are held in localised positions in the soil over long periods of time.

Substances can reach the soil by deposition from air. Sometimes they come down as solid particles or liquid droplets; not infrequently they are borne down by rain water as is the case with strontium 90. Soils in the neighbourhood of factory chimneys become contaminated with particles of soot and mineral matter whilst those near roads tend to be high in lead released from car exhausts. Agricultural soils often receive considerable quantities of substances used for pest and weed control, such materials being applied as sprays or dusts in most cases. However, not all of the pesticide reaches the land as the result of deliberate application. Material may fall a long way from its intended destination as the result of spray drift, whilst traces of pesticides present in the air can be carried down by rain.

Many substances are strongly persistent in soils. A number of factors influence this, and it is necessary to give brief consideration to the properties of soils by way of explanation.

The non-living fraction of most soils accounts for more than 95 per cent of the total dry weight, and may be divided into organic matter and inorganic matter. Much of the soil organic matter is synthesised by micro-organisms from organic residues and is termed humus. Humus is fairly stable chemically and is composed of units of colloidal size (less than 0·002 mm in diameter). It is rich in carboxyl and phenolic groups, which ionise to produce negatively charged exchange sites. Cations such as Ca^{2+}, K^+ and Na^+ are associated with them (Figure 1.2). Apart from relatively weak

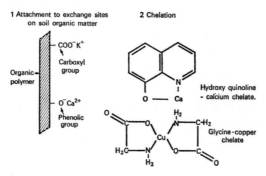

Fig. 1.2 Interaction between cations and organic groups

interactions of this kind, some divalent and trivalent cations are more strongly bound to humus and to certain soluble organic molecules in the soil. Chelation reactions are often responsible for his kind of binding (Figure 1.2). The polyvalent cation is held by two separate groups of an organic chelate with the formation of a ring structure. Monovalent ions do not generally form such complexes.

The inorganic particles of the soil are classified according to size, and the colloidal fraction, termed the clay fraction, is particularly important in the present context. Most of the particles in this fraction are clay minerals, produced by the weathering of rocks. They have complex lattice structures based on the elements silicon, aluminium and oxygen together with smaller quantities of iron, magnesium and other elements (Figure 1.3). The lattices are arranged into layers which bear negative charges. Various cations and water find their way between the layers; the cations balance the negative charge of the layers and are generally 'exchangeable', i.e. they are displaceable by other ions. In addition to these cation-exchange sites, there

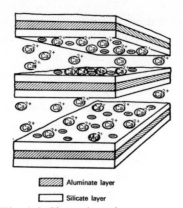

Aluminate layer

Silicate layer

Fig. 1.3 Clay mineral structure
The structure shown is that of a montmorillonite clay.
It has a very high capacity for holding cations between its
layers. This is because aluminium is extensively replaced
by divalent ions such as magnesium and iron, leaving the
lattice with a net negative charge.

are a limited number of positively charged anion-exchange sites in the clay fraction of the soil.

It should now be clear that there are a number of ways in which pollutants may be bound in soils. In the first place, many organic substances are tightly bound to either or both of the colloidal fractions by adsorption. Compounds are said to be adsorbed when they are held at a surface by physical forces (Van der Waal forces) that are not associated with any chemical bonding of a specific nature. Interactions occur over the whole surface of contact and although the forces operating at individual points are weak, the overall attraction can be very strong. Colloids have a very large surface area in relation to their volume, and are accordingly effective adsorbents for a variety of organic molecules. Studies on herbicides have demonstrated the importance of adsorption in connection with the retention of diverse molecules by soils.

Pollutants that exist as ions may be associated with charged sites in the soil. Pb^{2+}, Cu^{2+}, Hg^{2+} and Zn^{2+} and radioactive Sr^{2+} have all given rise to pollution problems, and are all held by the negatively charged exchange sites on organic matter and clays. There is evidence that Cu^{2+} and Zn^{2+} are also tightly bound to organic compounds in the soil by chelation. The herbicide paraquat exists as a positively charged ion and this is strongly held on the negatively charged surfaces within clay minerals. Bound in this way, it is not displaced by other cations or effectively broken down by soil micro-organisms. When paraquat is applied to soil, it is only active for a short time before it disappears into the clay minerals.

In view of the variety of ways in which pollutants may be bound to soil components, it is hardly surprising that they are not effectively removed from soils by leaching in the majority of cases. Such factors as breakdown to simpler components by bacteria, volatilisation and uptake by vegetation are important in determining their rate of disappearance from soils.

The metabolic capacity of a soil can be changed by the addition of various compounds. When certain herbicides such as 2,4D and MCPA are applied to a soil not previously treated in this way there follows a 'lag period' during which breakdown of the chemical is slow. This may continue for several weeks before the rate speeds up, and the molecule disappears from the soil (Figure 1.4). The increased metabolic

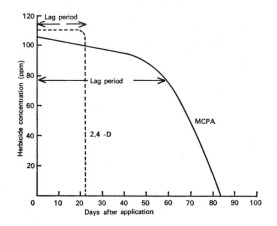

Fig. 1.4 Breakdown of herbicides in soil (After L. J. Audus, *Physiology and Biochemistry of Herbicides*)

rate is associated with an increase in the metabolic activity of certain micro-organisms. Once this has happened the soil is said to be in an 'enriched' state and is able to carry out rapid degradation of the herbicide as soon as further additions are made. It is not clear, however, to what extent enrichment is due to the rapid multiplication of pre-existing strains capable of attacking the compound or to the development of 'adaptive enzymes' (see Chapter II). If no further applications of herbicide substrate are made to the soil, the enrichment is slowly lost. Nevertheless, some increased metabolic activity can still be found even after one year without treatment. The 'enrichment' of a soil is not necessarily specific for the compound inducing the state; often related compounds experience no lag period before the onset of rapid degradation.

Little is known about the breakdown of pesticides and other pollutants by purely chemical processes in the soil. It is clear that certain oxidative and hydrolytic changes may proceed in the absence of living organisms. Thus aldrin is oxidised to dieldrin under the influence of light at the soil surface, and some triazine herbicides are hydrolysed under soil conditions. pH and degree of absorption by soil colloids are factors which can affect the rate of breakdown by non-biological agencies.

Dieldrin, DDT and BHC provide examples of compounds that are strongly persistent in soils. Unlike herbicides such as 2,4D and MCPA they are not rapidly removed from soils following 'enrichment'; this is probably due, at least in part, to their strong adsorption by soil colloids and their insolubility, factors which limit their availability to micro-organisms. After application to soil the rate of disappearance of organochlorine insecticides is not constant (Figure 1.5). Much material is lost

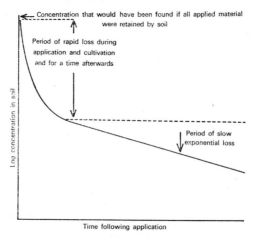

Fig. 1.5 Disappearance of persistent organochlorine insecticides from soils
(After C. A. Edwards, *Residue Reviews* 13)

by volatilisation or simply by being blown away as dust during the course of application and working into the soil. Thus there is a rapid initial rate of loss which eventually slackens off and gives way to a slower rate of disappearance as the insecticide becomes adsorbed by soil colloids. At this stage there is a straight-line relationship between time and the logarithm of the residual concentration. Data of this kind have been used to estimate the time necessary for a fixed percentage of the applied dose to disappear (see Chapter V).

Of the different sectors of the environment the soil contrasts with the air and the surface waters in several respects. Pollutants within the soil are not usually very mobile, whereas they move freely in air and water, often over great distances. By comparison with the air, the soil is chemically and biologically complex. Foreign compounds interact with minerals, organic matter, and living organisms within it. The manner of their degradation and binding is determined by these interactions and requires careful study in the appraisal of pollution problems.

II

Foreign Compounds and
Living Organisms

A COMPOUND may be considered as 'foreign' when it plays no part in the normal biochemistry of a particular organism. Since species differ from one another in their metabolism, a normal compound to one organism may be foreign to another. It follows that the process of ingesting such compounds must be nearly as old as life itself. Many substances of natural origin possess biological activity, and are sometimes useful as drugs or pesticides on this account. When they are ingested by animals there is a risk of death or sub-lethal poisoning if elimination is not rapid. Animals possess detoxication mechanisms which are involved in the removal of foreign compounds and these may have evolved in response to the selective pressure of noxious substances entering the body. It is not always clear, however, if such systems were originally concerned with the removal of endogenous substances, e.g. steroids, and became adapted to the elimination of exogenous foreign compounds at a later stage. Be this as it may, living organisms show a remarkable capacity for the metabolism and excretion of complex man-made molecules even when exposed to them for the first time.

The elimination of foreign compounds concerns not only the biochemical systems for degrading them but also the processes controlling their distribution and excretion. The fate of a pollutant within individuals and species is fundamental to the complex question of its distribution throughout an entire living system. Substances that are biologically persistent can be passed from organism to organism along a food chain and the long-term consequences of this are hard to determine, let alone foresee.

The processes of absorption, distribution, metabolism and excretion will now be discussed before considering effects of foreign compounds upon individuals and populations.

Movement across natural barriers

The absorption, distribution, and excretion of foreign compounds by living organisms is limited by barriers which are typically membranous in character. Individual cells contain a number of membranes, e.g. the nuclear membranes, the mitochondrial membranes, the endoplasmic reticulum and the plasma membrane. More complex barriers are made up of groups of cells which may be one layer thick (e.g. intestinal epithelium and hepatic parenchyma) or several layers thick (e.g. mammalian skin). Sometimes barriers consist of purely chemical layers with no cellular structure (e.g. the waxy layers of the plant cuticle and the insect epicuticle).

The membranes of the cell are lipoprotein structures containing a fairly constant proportion of 'bimodal' lipid (i.e. lipids such as lecithin which have both polar and non-polar parts). A unit membrane structure has been proposed to describe the basic organisation of all cell membranes (Figure 2.1). Although some controversy

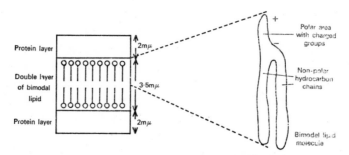

Fig. 2.1 Unit membrane structure

still exists, its essential features are widely accepted by scientists. It consists of a lipoprotein sandwich 7·5 mμ thick with a double layer of bimodal lipid bounded to either side by a layer of protein. The polar groups of the lipid molecules are directed towards the protein layer, whilst the non-polar ends join one another in the middle of the sandwich. The model can accommodate a wide range of different lipids and proteins into the same basic organisation. The existence of pores through the membrane is not excluded.

The movement of substances through membranes may be by passive diffusion, active transport, facilitated diffusion, endocytosis or mass flow.

Passive diffusion involves the spontaneous movement of substances without the assistance of metabolic energy or carrier molecules. A distinction is made between substances that appear to move passively through pores containing water molecules and those that dissolve in the membrane. Substances in the first group are either inorganic ions such as Cl^- or small water soluble molecules like urea and ethanol. By contrast, larger organic molecules often move through the membrane itself and many pollutants behave in this way.

A degree of fat solubility favours the movement of large organic molecules across membranes, whereas high water solubility due to charged groups or strong polarity does not. This behaviour is to be expected when diffusion is through a lipoprotein structure, especially if there are polar/non-polar interfaces as are proposed in the unit membrane theory. Some very non-polar substances like cholesterol and the insecticide dieldrin move freely into membranes but do not readily come out.

Whilst it is broadly true that a balance between fat and water solubility assists penetration, it should not be assumed that all membranes behave in the same way. This is not so even with simple cell membranes, let alone the variety of more complex barriers (e.g. skin, insect cuticle) across which organic molecules pass.

Active transport is characterised by the use of metabolic energy to move substances across membranes. Typically the direction of movement is counter to that which is possible by passive diffusion. In physico-chemical terms, uncharged molecules are moved against their chemical potential gradients, ions against their electrochemical potential gradients, and both processes require a supply of energy to make substances travel 'uphill'. Ions such as Na^+ and K^+, and a number of endogenous molecules are actively transported in living animals. The movement of penicillin across the tubular wall of the kidney is one of the few known cases of active transport of foreign compounds.

Facilitated diffusion differs from active transport in that the movement of substances is normally in the direction expected for passive diffusion and is not directly dependent upon metabolic energy. The rate of movement, however, is too great to be explained by this process. The penetration of the red cell membrane by glucose and other sugars provides one example of facilitated diffusion. In this case a carrier molecule is thought to aid movement across the membrane. The process does not seem to be important for foreign compounds.

Small particles or droplets are sometimes absorbed directly into cells by *endocytosis*. They are engulfed by the plasma membrane and the invagination so formed is cut off, releasing the contents into the cell (Figure 2.2). Endocytosis has been observed in cells of the intestinal epithelium. It may be important in the absorption of foreign compounds from the alimentary tract.

Many water soluble substances pass through the glomerular membrane of the kidney by ultra filtration. *Mass flow* of water through membrane pores carries soluble molecules up to a certain size into the tubular lumen. Quite large molecules, e.g. Haemoglobin mol.wt. 60,000, may be excreted in this way. Substances are carried through the walls of blood capillaries into lymph by a similar process.

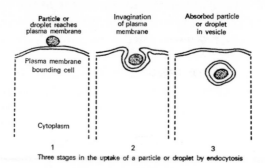

Fig. 2.2 Endocytosis

Absorption of foreign compounds

Substances gain entry into living organisms by crossing barriers that are often thin layers of cells. In animals, absorption takes place across the gut wall or across the skin or integument; aerial pollutants enter through the lungs of vertebrates, and substances dissolved or suspended in water through the gills of fish. Micro-organisms absorb substances through their cell walls whilst plants absorb through the cells of their roots or leaves.

Uptake from the gut is of particular interest to pharmacologists and has been closely studied. Liposoluble substances generally move across the gut membranes by passive diffusion. In this context the behaviour of weak acids and bases is influenced by pH. Thus a weak acid such as aspirin exists largely in the undissociated state in the mammalian stomach due to the high hydrogen ion concentration (pH 2–3) which pushes the equilibrium from right to left.

Aspirin
(Acetyl salicylic acid)   Acetyl salicylate ion

The undissociated acid is much more fat soluble than its anion (conjugate base) and moves much more rapidly across the gastric membrane. By the same argument, many weak acids are not readily absorbed across the intestinal epithelium because the pH there is rather high and the anionic form predominates. The ratio of charged to uncharged forms of weak acids and bases at different pH's may be calculated from the Henderson–Hasselbalch equation.

22

For acids: $$pK_a - pH = \log \frac{(\text{conc. dissociated form})}{(\text{conc. undissociated form})}$$

For bases: $$pK_a - pH = \log \frac{(\text{conc. undissociated form})}{(\text{conc. dissociated form})}$$

Where K_a = acid constant

$pK_a = -\log_{10} K_a$

Although some intestinal absorption of foreign compounds appears to take place by endocytosis and active transport, passive diffusion seems to be more important in most cases.

The efficiency with which the lungs absorb many gases is illustrated by the rapidity with which inhaled carbon monoxide (CO) and hydrogen cyanide (HCN) can cause death. In addition to gases, materials present in the air as particles or droplets may also be absorbed in this way. For this reason, it is often necessary for operators of agricultural spray machinery to wear masks. Similarly, pollutants of urban air, such as inorganic lead and carcinogenic polycyclic aromatic hydrocarbons, have been investigated as possible hazards to public health.

Absorption across the insect cuticle provides the basis for the useful contact action of many insecticides. Although the cuticle is not membranous it does contain polar/non-polar interfaces (Figure 2.3) which must be negotiated by molecules

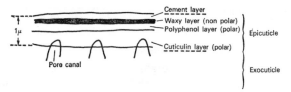

Fig. 2.3 Structure of insect cuticle

entering by this route. The penetration of the insect cuticle by insecticides and other foreign molecules is influenced by the form in which they are presented. Some molecules of fairly low fat solubility can still traverse the cuticle if they are first dissolved in an organic liquid which gets them into the non-polar waxy layer. In general, penetration of the cuticle appears to be passive. For some substances the permeability of the cuticle is similar to that of the mammalian skin, a point that needs to be borne in mind by users of contact insecticides. The pore channels through the insect cuticle may also be important in the absorption of foreign compounds, but this has yet to be properly investigated.

Aquatic organisms can absorb dissolved or dispersed fat soluble substances directly from water. The gills of fish and the skin of amphibia behave as typical lipoprotein barriers, and many fat soluble compounds pass freely across them.

Some substances reach similar concentrations in the body fluids of fish and amphibia to those present in the surrounding medium. This indicates that uptake is by a passive diffusion process tending towards equilibrium. On the other hand, there are substances that get tightly bound to soluble proteins in body fluids. This can lead to higher concentrations being reached in body fluids than are established by diffusion alone. The gills of crustacea are not lipoprotein structures, and by contrast with fish, fat soluble molecules do not pass freely across.

The uptake of foreign compounds by plants requires mention. Fat soluble molecules usually cross the waxy cuticle of the leaf by passive diffusion. Water soluble substances are often readily taken up by the leaf, and it is believed that they enter through the stomata in aqueous solution. Green stems behave similarly to leaves, but penetration through the bark of woody stems can be very difficult. The capacity of roots to take up water soluble compounds from the soil has been exploited in the development of soil-acting herbicides. Although active transport systems are important in the uptake of inorganic ions by roots, it is not known whether this mechanism is also important for foreign compounds such as these.

Finally, it should be mentioned that algae, protozoa and other lowly organisms can absorb many different substances from the surrounding medium across the cell wall.

Movement and storage

Foreign compounds such as insecticides and fungicides which travel in the vascular system of plants are termed 'systemic'. Such compounds are often rather water soluble and not usually very fat soluble. Animals, on the other hand, transport many highly fat soluble compounds in the blood or haemolymph without difficulty. Usually soluble proteins or other components of these fluids act as carriers for them.

The distribution of noxious substances within animals influences the extent to which they become available to their sites of action, to the biochemical systems that degrade them and to the organs that can excrete them. Storage in compartments of the body where they are not metabolised can limit their availability, at least in the short term. Storage fat is such a compartment. Compounds with high fat solubility tend to be stored in this tissue without being degraded. The rate of mobilisation of depot fat influences their rate of release from store and consequently their availability to other compartments of the body. When fat soluble poisons are stored in depot fat there is a danger that they will display latent toxicity, i.e. symptoms will develop after exposure to the poison has ceased, a problem that will be discussed later in this chapter. The retention of Pb^{2+} by bone is another example of the way in which storage can keep a poison from its site of action – at least in the short term.

The storage of active compounds can also have beneficial consequences. For example, the long-term action of the trypanocidal drug, suramin, is attributed to its strong binding to albumin in the blood. It is protected from many potentially harmful substances by the blood-brain barrier and blood–cerebrospinal fluid barrier. (These terms refer to physiological phenomena rather than anatomical structures.) The rate of movement of organic molecules across them is usually proportional to their fat solubility with the exception of one or two substances which are taken up actively. Thus weak acids such as aspirin, which are readily absorbed from the stomach due to the low pH obtaining there, show little tendency to cross the blood-brain barrier, because they exist mainly in the anionic form at the normal physiological pH values. The exit of foreign compounds from the brain is but poorly understood. No doubt loss may occur by passive diffusion, but filtration of compounds across the arachnoid villi could be more important.

Excretion

A compound may be eliminated from the body unchanged, or as a breakdown product (metabolite) or conjugate (p. 27).

The efficiency with which a foreign compound is excreted often depends upon its metabolic fate. Fat soluble substances, for example, tend to be stored in the fat depots of the body, and excretion is very slow unless they are changed into more water soluble substances. Thus when they are metabolised their distribution is altered.

The functioning of the excretory system is often associated with the question of water conservation. Where it is important for animals to conserve water, reabsorption from urine within the body is almost complete, and in insects, reptiles and birds the remaining waste products are voided with the faeces. On the other hand, mammals do not concentrate urine to this extent, neither do they excrete their urinary waste products with the faeces. Urine is eliminated independently of the faeces, and this can result in a considerable water loss to the animal.

In higher animals, the principle routes for elimination of foreign compounds are via the urine or faeces. Substances move from the blood into the kidney tubules in two distinct ways; by filtration through the membrane of Bowman's capsule, or by movement across the tubular wall (Figure 2.4). Passage across the tubular wall is commonly by passive diffusion, although some active transport also occurs in the proximal tubule. Movement by passive diffusion is related to fat solubility and is commonly encountered with foreign compounds.

As urine passes along the renal tubules, certain substances are reabsorbed. Not infrequently the pH falls with passage down the tubules which leads to the formation of undissociated weak acids from their anions. These are then reabsorbed into the blood stream by passive diffusion together with other fat soluble molecules.

The excretion of substances into bile can lead to their final elimination in faeces.

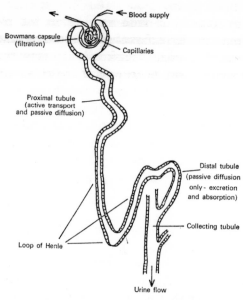

Diagrammatic representation of nephron

← Blood supply

Bowmans capsule
(filtration)

Capillaries

Proximal tubule
(active transport
and passive diffusion)

Distal tubule
(passive diffusion
only - excretion
and absorption)

Collecting tubule

Loop of Henle

Urine flow

Fig. 2.4 Excretion by the kidney

This process is closely linked to metabolic events in the liver, where water soluble conjugates are formed. Conjugates with molecular weights greater than 300 are readily moved into bile and so into the gut. If they are not degraded, they are not usually reabsorbed and tend to pass straight out of the body with the faeces. If, on the other hand, they are hydrolysed in the gut, non-polar hydrolysis products are liable to be reabsorbed, returned to the liver, reconjugated and excreted again into the bile, a process termed enterohepatic circulation. Clearly this can be an obstacle to speedy elimination of active compounds. Unfortunately it has not been widely investigated so its significance with regard to retention of pollutants is largely unknown.

Although the conversion of fat soluble compounds to water soluble metabolites aids excretion in mammals, it is not clear how far this is the case in fish and amphibia. These groups appear to have rather poorly developed metabolic systems for degrading certain foreign compounds and many fat soluble compounds are 'excreted' across the gills or skin just as easily as they are taken up (q.v.).

Finally, there are a number of less important excretory routes used by the vertebrate animal. Volatile liquids such as chloroform, alcohol and ether may be expelled from the lungs as vapours together with water and carbon dioxide. Certain organic substances are also eliminated in milk, eggs and sweat.

26

Metabolism of foreign compounds

Living organisms show extraordinary versatility in metabolising foreign molecules even when as individuals or species they encounter them for the first time. Commonly, active compounds such as drugs or poisons are transformed into less active metabolites, although there are a number of instances where metabolites are more active than their parent compounds. Where this is so, metabolic conversion is described as 'activating' as opposed to 'deactivating'.

Fat soluble compounds are nearly always transformed into more polar, and therefore more water soluble, metabolites. The significance of this with regard to distribution and excretion should be clear from the foregoing discussion.

Metabolic transformations frequently occur in two stages:

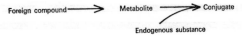

The conjugate is formed by coupling the metabolite with a polar endogenous* molecule, and is usually readily excreted. There are departures from this scheme however, since foreign compounds can be conjugated directly and metabolites can be excreted without further change.

The biochemical systems of vertebrates which break down foreign compounds have been widely studied and demand particular attention. Although present in many tissues, they are particularly abundant in the liver. Most of the relevant enzyme systems are found in the endoplasmic reticulum of the hepatic cells (Figure 2.5).

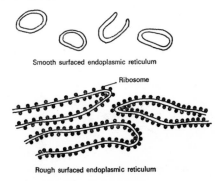

Fig. 2.5 The endoplasmic reticulum

As seen under the electron microscope, this exists as a membranous network running through the cytoplasm. The rough-surfaced endoplasmic reticulum has granules (ribosomes) associated with it; the smooth-surfaced endoplasmic reticulum has not. Both structures are released from liver cells when broken up by homogenisation and are brought out of suspension by high-speed contrifugation. The precipitate so

* Synthesised within the organism

formed is termed the microsomal fraction and consists largely of vesicles (microsomes) derived from the membranous network. Microsomal preparations are widely used in the investigation of the metabolic systems of the endoplasmic reticulum.

The uptake of fat soluble compounds by vertebrates is commonly followed by an increase in liver size. Sometimes this is due to liver damage but more often it reflects a physiological response which has a protective function. In the latter case, liver enlargement is accompanied by a proliferation of the smooth-surfaced endoplasmic reticulum and a corresponding increase in the metabolic activity of the organ towards many foreign molecules. The liver enzymes are said to be 'induced' and this leads to an increased rate of metabolism and elimination of many fat soluble foreign compounds.

Hepatic microsomal enzymes are noteworthy for their versatility. They can attack a wide spectrum of fat soluble compounds by oxidation, reduction, hydrolysis and hydration. They also promote a number of conjugation reactions.

Oxidations by microsomes are of particular interest and are mediated by a group of hypothetical* microsomal oxidases.

The following examples illustrate the wide variety of microsomal oxidations:

Parathion
(organophosphate insecticide)

Paraoxon

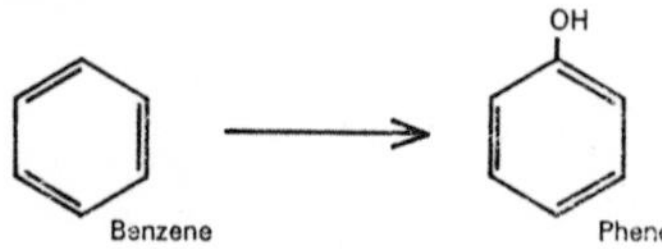

Benzene

Phenol

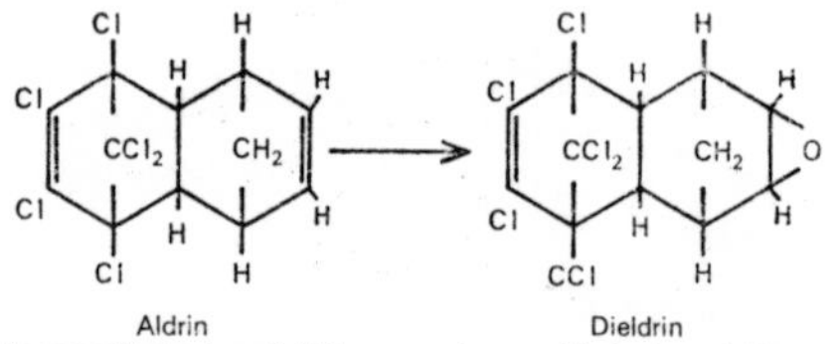

Aldrin
(organochlorine insecticide)

Dieldrin
(organochlorine insecticide)

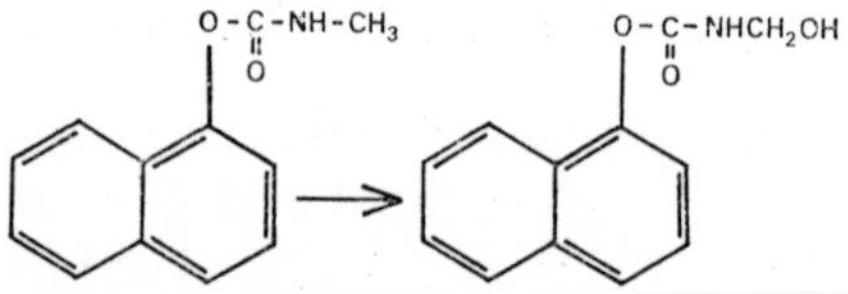

Carbaryl (carbamate insecticide)   Hydroxymethyl carbaryl

* Hypothetical in the sense that they are named after a great number of individual metabolic conversions carried out by intact microsomes for which no specific enzymes have been isolated, e.g. hexobarbitone oxidase (oxidation of the drug hexobarbitone)

28

Conversions 1 and 3 are activating; the metabolites are more toxic than the original compounds.

A number of foreign molecules are attacked by hydrolytic and hydrative microsomal systems. In the following examples, paraoxon is hydrolysed, and dieldrin is hydrated, yielding metabolites of greater water solubility than the original substrates.

The microsomal hydration of dieldrin takes place slowly and has only been demonstrated so far with rabbit and pig liver preparations.

Conjugations have already been mentioned in connection with excretion via the bile. Liver microsomes perform a number of these reactions if provided with appropriate co-factors. In the example given, glucuronic acid is transferred from a complex endogenous molecule (UDPGA) to phenol under the influence of a microsomal enzyme.

UDPGA is produced in the soluble fraction of the cell and must be available to microsomes before conjugation can occur; the reaction cannot be carried out by microsomes alone. A number of steroids and other endogenous substances are conjugated in a similar manner prior to excretion via the bile.

Not all metabolic conversions depend upon the endoplasmic reticulum. There are a number of enzymes that can hydrolyse esters (esterases) in the body fluids and soluble fractions of cells and some of these can attack foreign compounds. Organophosphate esters, for example, are broken down by enzymes of this type. Apart from the endoplasmic reticulum other cell membranes and organelles have not been very widely investigated in this context. Lysosomes are cell organelles that seem to be of importance in degrading foreign compounds. They contain, for example, certain hydrolytic enzymes that can attack synthetic esters.

Micro-organisms in general and bacteria in particular play an important role in the breakdown of environmental pollutants in soils, surface waters and muds associated with lakes and rivers. As we have seen, the appearance of certain pollutants in soil can lead to an upsurge of bacteria able to metabolise them; the bacterial flora can be altered, at least temporarily, by a chemical factor. It is also possible for individual bacteria to adapt to unfamiliar organic substances in their environment. Sometimes they can develop enzyme systems to metabolise new molecules. Such enzymes are termed adaptive or inducible enzymes.

An appreciation of the metabolic capacity of individual species is useful when considering the fate of chemicals in the environment. There are, however, difficulties in moving from the relatively simple metabolic studies of the laboratory to the complexities of the field situation. Here one is dealing with dozens of fat soluble foreign compounds at measurable concentrations which may interact with one another. The metabolic fate of any one chemical may be influenced by the presence of other chemicals. One foreign compound may speed up the metabolism of another by causing induction of liver enzymes. For this to happen, the two compounds need not both be present at the same time. The organ may retain its enhanced activity for some time after the inducing compound has been completely metabolised. It has been pointed out that induction of liver enzymes results in an increased rate of reaction for a wide range of substances. In the case of drugs and poisons this often means a reduction in their effectiveness since the majority of the microsomal conversions are de-activating, although there are important exceptions to this generalisation.

Interaction between foreign compounds can be more direct. A number of compounds are known which are powerful inhibitors of microsomal systems at low concentrations. The metabolism of many other substances is strongly retarded by their presence with important consequences when biological activity is involved. Thus drugs and poisons are made more effective if their de-activation is slowed down, but less effective if their activation is inhibited. Some compounds of low toxicity such as piperonyl butoxide can inhibit microsomal oxidases. When included in certain insecticide formulations they stabilise the active ingredient within the target organism by retarding its breakdown. The toxicity of the insecticide is increased by piperonyl butoxide and the phenomenon is termed synergism.

In addition to induction and synergism, competition for storage sites and indirect effects following from physiological changes are further examples of ways in which metabolism of one substance may be affected by the action of another. Little is known of these interactions in relatively simple laboratory situations; their significance in the field is purely a matter of conjecture.

Biological persistence

The stability of a compound in the gross environment is no guarantee of its long life following entry into an animal. Enzymatic attack can cause the rapid breakdown of compounds that are quite stable in other respects. Thus the insecticide γBHC (lindane) is very persistent in soils but is quickly eliminated by vertebrates, largely as a result of rapid metabolism.

The biological persistence of substances is measured in terms of their half lives which give a measure of the rate of disappearance of a substance within an animal consequent upon its metabolic breakdown and its direct excretion. A certain dose is first given to an animal, administration is discontinued and the rate of disappearance determined. The log of the concentration of the compound in a suitable tissue is plotted against time following dosing to give a straight-line relationship from which the half life may be deduced.

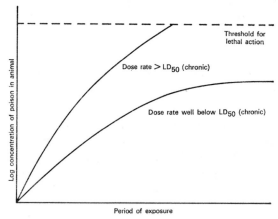

Fig. 2.6 Accumulation of persistent poisons within animals

Strong biological persistence poses problems over and above those connected with such persistence in the inorganic environment. Regular assimilation of small doses can lead to long-term build-up of concentration within the body. In the simplest case, a constant rate of intake is accompanied by a steady rise in internal concentration. As the concentration increases so does the rate of metabolism and excretion. Eventually, if a lethal concentration is not reached, the rate of elimination will come to balance the rate of absorption, with the establishment of a plateau level (Figure 2.6). This is a highly simplified picture and does not take into account the consequences of any change in the rate of metabolism. If liver enzymes are induced, for example, the rate of build-up may be reduced or even reversed. Notwithstanding such complications, one point of general interest emerges – continuous ingestion of a persistent compound does not inevitably lead to the attainment of a lethal concentration. Whether it does so or not depends upon the dose absorbed, the susceptibility of the animal and its capacity to eliminate the compound.

If an animal is not killed by chronic (i.e. long-term) exposure to a persistent compound there is still the possibility that it will suffer sub-lethal effects. Indeed these may represent a more serious threat to the survival of the species than straightforward lethal effects. A decline in reproductive success, for example, may be more damaging to a population than a small annual loss due to lethal poisoning.

The hazards associated with biological persistence extend beyond the fate of individual organisms. Highly persistent compounds such as the organochlorine insecticide dieldrin are passed along food chains to become widely dispersed through-out the living environment. The way in which such distribution occurs is clearly influenced by the capacity of different species to break pollutants down. Species of poor metabolic capacity represent points in the food network where pollutants may build up (i.e. where they may reach a higher concentration in the organism than is present in its diet). In this context, organisms which are the most efficient accumulators of poisons are not necessarily those that are most vulnerable to toxic action. This may be the fate of other species that occupy higher positions in the food network and which suffer the consequences of amplification of concentration occurring in lower trophic levels.

Harmful effects of foreign compounds

The most dramatic consequence of absorbing a foreign compound is death, but there are a variety of sub-lethal effects which may precede this event. Generally speaking, lethal effects are easier to study than sub-lethal effects, especially when investigation is in the field rather than the laboratory. Whichever effects one is studying, however, it is of paramount importance to establish the connection between dose and response. In this way, it may be possible to define a 'no-effect' level below which no response can be found, as well as the risks associated with particular concentrations.

A typical dose–response curve is given in Figure 2.7(a). The response in this case is the percentage kill in a group of experimental animals receiving a particular dose of a poison expressed as milligrams per kilogram body weight. The relationship between log dose and response is linear over most of the range but this does not hold good at the extremes of the graph. Where 'dose' is expressed in terms of concentration in the surrounding medium, the appearance of toxic symptoms is often slow. It is therefore necessary to record the percentage kill after different periods of exposure to varying levels of a poison (Figure 2.7(b)).

Once a dose–response curve has been constructed it is possible to read off either the applied dose (LD_{50}) or the concentration (LC_{50} or median lethal concentration) responsible for a 50 per cent kill. This gives a standard measurement of toxicity. In the case of LD_{50} determinations, a distinction is made between short-term and long-term toxic action. An acute LD_{50} is measured after administration of a single

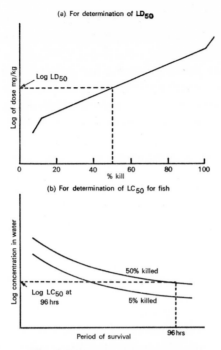

Fig. 2.7 Dose–response curves

dose, whereas a chronic LD_{50} refers to longer term toxic action following two or more doses given at different times. Since LC_{50} values based on concentration in ambient medium tend to be long-term measurements of toxicity they are more comparable to chronic then acute LD_{50} values.

In dose-response curves, percentage kill in a group of animals increases over a considerable concentration range until it reaches 100 per cent. This shows the variation in susceptibility that exists between individuals, and points to the need for relatively large numbers of subjects and careful statistical analysis when determining dose–response curves. Indeed it can be argued that even very small doses may prove lethal to certain individuals. Where an animal is suffering from disease, for example, very little poison may be required to cause death. This raises the question of how valid 'no-effect' levels are as determined from dose–response curves. 'No-effect' levels should be seen in relation to the errors of the experiment and it is possible that many would have to be lowered if experimental accuracy were improved. The problem of 'no-effect' levels in human beings is a particularly difficult one, the more so since direct experimentation is precluded.

Dose–response curves, LD_{50}s and LC_{50}s, are all useful for studying environmental effects of pollutants. In studying river pollution in relation to fish and other aquatic organisms, LC_{50} values are useful especially when related to time. Time is also taken into account by the California State Department of Public Health in fixing air quality standards (see Chapter VII).

LC_{50} values for air and water give some indication of the toxic effects that may be produced by various concentrations of pollutants. Frequently, however, the problem lies in determining the cause of death when examining carcasses from a suspected case of pollution. Here it is desirable to have dose–response curves linking the tissue concentration of pollutants with their toxic effects. It should be added that the measurement of tissue concentration has an important advantage over an estimate of applied dose when considering toxic action. The individual members of a species vary widely regarding efficiency of absorption from the gut and this introduces an experimental error that is avoided if concentration is measured within the animal.

It is now time to turn from lethal to sub-lethal effects. It is incorrect to assume that there is a clear division between a 'no-effect' level and a lethal level. In practice, many poisons produce clear sub-lethal effects before they reach a lethal concentration, e.g. organochlorine insecticides can cause muscular spasms, disturbances in egg shell formation and hyperthyroidism in birds at sub-lethal concentrations. The sub-lethal effects seen during intake of a poison are often reversible at the time of their first appearance and will disappear if exposure is discontinued. If the level of poison continues to rise, the effects become irreversible and eventually a lethal concentration is reached.

In general, the effect of a foreign compound upon a living organism is seldom simple. Most drugs produce various side effects distinct from their intended pharmacological action, and it would be surprising if environmental pollutants did not present a similar picture. A number of environmental pollutants can have effects upon the nervous system, an action that is likely to trigger off a number of secondary responses. Organophosphate nerve poisons, for example, can cause behavioural disturbances in fish at levels too low for chemical detection. Thus it is probable that a great number of sub-lethal effects are caused by pollutants. The difficulty arises in identifying and measuring them and in assessing their significance.

Significance of pollutants in the environment

Unlike most laboratory experiments, studies in the living environment are not closely controlled by the investigator; that is to say, they are largely observational, with only limited opportunities for altering factors with a view to measuring response. Frequently, different parameters are measured and correlations are sought between them – for example the residues of a persistent pollutant in a species may be set against a population decline. Where such correlations are found, they need to be treated with caution for they do not necessarily point to causal relationships. It is possible to get good correlations between parameters that are not directly related.

For example there is a very good correlation between the incidence of lung cancer and the introduction of street lighting.

Controlled laboratory experiments may be used to establish whether correlations observed in the field actually represent causal relationships. Thus toxicological studies can relate levels of pollutants in animal tissues to lethal and sub-lethal effects and the data can be used to decide whether a residue level found in the field is causing a population decline. Although straightforward in theory, this is difficult in practice, and there are many pitfalls to overcome.

Heavy mortalities of wild animals and birds have sometimes been associated with residues of persistent poisons in the carcasses. The mere presence of a poison, however, does not prove that it is the cause of death. It is necessary to know the connection between the concentration of poison and the expected lethal effect, i.e. a dose–response curve is required; but here there are problems. Very often, as in forensic science, it is not possible to experiment with the species in question and data obtained from another species must be used instead. Unless a carcase, is fresh it is very likely that residue concentrations will have changed since death due to dehydration of tissues, or post mortem breakdown or both. Furthermore it is difficult to simulate natural conditions in the laboratory. Stress, temperature, exercise and many other factors can affect an animal's response to a poison, and it is virtually impossible to make them operate in the same way in the laboratory as they do in the field. Toxicological data of this kind are therefore of limited usefulness and need to be seen in relation to other lines of evidence when interpreting events in the field.

Notwithstanding these objections, it is easier to study lethal effects than sub-lethal ones. As we have seen, there is reason to suppose that the sub-lethal effects of pollutants are commonplace but it is not easy to identify them, let alone measure them accurately. Chronic bronchitis brought on by air pollution, and eye irritation due to photochemical 'smog' are amongst the few cases that have been well established.

At the present time, many living organisms contain a variety of persistent pollutants, generally at very low concentrations. Organochlorine insecticides, polycyclic aromatic hydrocarbons and mercurial fungicides are classes of compounds widely represented and there are probably others awaiting discovery. Assessment of the overall lethal and sub-lethal effects of a group of persistent substances in the whole environment is not feasible. Induction of liver enzymes and synergism have already been discussed in connection with metabolism of foreign compounds, and these are both ways in which the level of one pollutant may be influenced by other pollutants within the same animal. There is also the question of the overall impact upon an animal of two or more compounds exercising separate toxic actions at the same time. To determine all the effects of all possible combinations of established pollutants would be a formidable problem even for one species, let alone for all living organisms.

In practice, then, it is necessary to be highly selective in choosing species and pollutants for study.

It is easier to interpret residue levels of a poison if the mode of action is known, but unfortunately this is seldom the case. The way in which organochlorine insecticides act is not properly explained in spite of their widespread dissemination and many other examples could be cited. Where mode of action is known it is often possible to define characteristic physiological and biochemical changes caused by the poison. The organophosphate insecticides, for example, are known to inhibit the enzyme acetylcholinesterase in vertebrates. Once inhibition has occurred its substrate acetylcholine is not broken down sufficiently quickly, and tends to build up at nerve synapses and the neuromuscular junction. Accumulation of acetylcholine leads to continuous muscular contraction (tetanus) and death. Inhibited acetylcholinesterase is fairly stable and it is possible to measure percentage inhibition in reasonably fresh carcasses. Percentage inhibition is closely related to toxic effect and can provide strong evidence for organophosphate poisoning in a post mortem examination. Thus it can be easier to identify toxic effects of pollutants by recognising characteristic physiological and biochemical changes rather than measuring levels of compounds which are extremely difficult to interpret. Furthermore, such an understanding of mode of action can be valuable in anticipating and avoiding harmful effects of environmental contamination.

So far, the discussion has been limited to lethal and sub-lethal effects of pollutants and their recognition. To the ecologist these matters are subordinate to a more crucial issue – the long-term effects of pollutants upon populations. Once a toxic effect has been identified and measured, be it a percentage mortality of a percentage decline in reproductive success, its impact on the species must be assessed. Even with straightforward mortality this requires careful investigation. Species such as the wood pigeon can survive losses of up to 90 per cent in one season without any effect upon numbers in the succeeding year (see p. 90), whereas certain predators are much more sensitive to high mortality. Again, it is quite possible that sub-lethal effects upon reproduction and behaviour may be more important than lethal effects for certain species. The solution of problems such as these depends upon the collaborative effort of scientists from many different disciplines including ecology, toxicology, chemistry, physiology and biochemistry.

III

Atmospheric Pollution
by Gases

M OST gases causing air pollution are products of fuel combustion and have been released into the atmosphere since man first burned wood and coal. As early as 1273 an Act of Parliament was passed prohibiting the burning of coal in London. Although this bears adequate testimony to the existence of pollutants such as sulphur dioxide in town air at that time, the legislation was primarily to control smoke, little being known about the chemistry of gases. Smoke is the visible product of incomplete combustion, and is inevitably accompanied by gases formed during the burning of fuels. Coal smoke consists of tiny particles averaging 0·075 μ in diameter which are of variable chemical composition consisting principally of carbon and tarry hydrocarbons. Although associated with gaseous pollutants, smoke, like atmospheric ash and dust, is best regarded as a physical pollutant. As such it lies outside of the scope of this book except in so far as it contains certain chemical pollutants, e.g. 3, 4 benzpyrene.

Unlike smoke, the gaseous products of fuel combustion are generally invisible and are in the same physical state as the air itself. Gaseous molecules are highly mobile and are completely miscible regardless of molecular species where there is no chemical interaction. Thus polluting gases tend to be more evenly distributed in the atmosphere than is smoke. Gases can be brought out of the air by solution in rain, mist droplets or surface waters.

The gases under discussion here are all naturally occurring and man has merely augmented their environmental levels by his activities. Lead tetra alkyls and organo-chlorine compounds in the vapour phase are examples of 'unnatural' polluting gases, which are considered in later chapters.

Fuels consist mainly of carbon and/or carbon compounds which liberate heat when burned in air. If the air supply is unlimited during combustion, the main gaseous product is carbon dioxide. On the other hand, shortage of air results in incomplete combustion and formation of carbon monoxide. Carbon dioxide is a colourless, odourless gas of negligible toxicity which dissolves in water to form carbonic acid. It is a vital component of the air although it normally represents only 0·04 per cent by volume of the atmosphere. Atmospheric carbon dioxide is being continually turned over. It is removed by photo-synthetic plants which incorporate it into complex organic molecules from which it is liberated by the respiration of plants and animals. It is released in relatively small quantities by the action of volcanoes and natural springs. With this in mind, can fuel-derived carbon dioxide be regarded as a pollutant? Some scientists believe so because the present rate of consumption of coal and other fossil fuels appears to be causing a slow increase in the carbon dioxide content of the atmosphere. They suggest that the level could rise by as much as 25 per cent in the next forty years. If this does happen there may be associated climatic changes. Alteration of the world's radiation balance and melting of the polar ice cap are possible consequences. The matter is highly controversial and will not be pursued further here.

Carbon monoxide, on the other hand, is a toxic gas of recognised importance as a pollutant. Vertebrates freely absorb it through the lungs, and it combines strongly with haemoglobin upon entering the bloodstream. It is held in the position on the haemoglobin molecule that is normally occupied by oxygen. The carboxy haemoglobin so formed shows little tendency to combine with oxygen, and the blood thereby loses some of its capacity for transporting this gas to the tissues when it absorbs carbon monoxide. Inhalation of air containing 1000 parts per million (ppm) of carbon monoxide quickly leads to serious inactivation of haemoglobin and rapid death due to anoxia. In this context, most fatal cases of carbon monoxide poisoning have between 50 per cent and 80 per cent of their total haemoglobin in the carboxy form. At relatively high levels carbon monoxide has a synergistic relationship with other toxic pollutants such as hydrogen sulphide or nitrogen dioxide. That is to say, the combined effect of carbon monoxide plus either of these gases is greater than the sum of the individual effects. For this reason, the gas cannot be considered in isolation from other pollutants when assessing toxic hazards.

The elimination of carbon monoxide is fairly rapid, and healthy subjects will lose half of their blood carbon monoxide within 3–4 hours of receiving a heavy dose. Because of this it has been suggested that carbon monoxide presents a more serious hazard in the short term than in the long term.

Carbon monoxide reaches quite high levels in the air of towns, largely as the result of release from car exhausts. It is less dense than air and disperses quite rapidly after emission. Nevertheless, levels as high as 100 ppm can exist locally over considerable periods of time when the gas is being continuously liberated. This can happen in enclosed spaces such as garages and tunnels, and sometimes in the open air if there is a traffic jam.

Most people experience dizziness, headache, lassitude and other symptoms of poisoning when they inhale air containing 100 ppm of carbon monoxide. Furthermore, certain individuals are highly susceptible to the gas, and for them such levels can be dangerous. Anaemic people with low haemoglobin levels fall into this category. These points have been taken into consideration by the California State Department of Public Health in defining Ambient Air Quality Standards (see Chapter VII). They define a 'serious' level of carbon monoxide in the air as 120 ppm for 1 hour or 30 ppm for 8 hours.

Cigarette smokers are exposed to higher carbon monoxide levels than nonsmokers, for the gas is formed during the combustion of tobacco. Susceptible individuals need to bear this in mind when they are already exposed to substantial levels of environmental carbon monoxide.

The long-term fate of atmospheric carbon monoxide is uncertain. In view of its low density it may be expected to rise to the higher levels of the atmosphere. Some oxidation to carbon dioxide occurs but the rate of change has never been determined and it is not known if the atmospheric level is increasing.

Sulphur dioxide (SO_2) is a gas of unpleasant odour formed by the combustion of sulphur, sulphides and various organic sulphur compounds. Sulphur trioxide (SO_3) is a volatile liquid formed in small quantities in the same way, and the two substances are usually found in association with each other.

Sulphur dioxide dissolves in water to form the unstable sulphurous acid which is readily oxidised to sulphuric acid by hydrogen peroxide, ferric ions and other oxidising agents.

$$SO_2 + H_2O \rightarrow H_2SO_3 \xrightarrow{O} H_2SO_4$$

Sulphur dioxide slowly oxidises to sulphur trioxide in the air, and this dissolves in water to form sulphuric acid directly.

$$SO_3 + H_2O \rightarrow H_2SO_4$$

When damp air is polluted with oxides of sulphur, droplets of water containing sulphurous and sulphuric acids are also present, causing a complex pattern of pollution.

Natural release of sulphur dioxide together with traces of sulphur trioxide follows volcanic action, whilst 'unnatural' release results from the burning of fuels. Coal, for example, contains 0·5–4·0 per cent sulphur, some of which is in the form of extraneous minerals such as iron pyrites (FeS_2) and inorganic sulphates. The burning of coal puts some six million tons of sulphur dioxide per annum into the atmosphere in Great Britain alone. Removal of extraneous sulphur-bearing minerals from coal is an effective way of reducing this pollution problem. Fuel oils also contain sulphur at rather similar levels, the highest concentrations being in residual oils from the distillation process.

Human beings are affected by quite low levels of sulphur dioxide in the air they breathe; 1–5 ppm causes discomfort, whilst exposure to 10 ppm for one hour usually results in severe distress. The Californian State Department of Health defines 5 ppm for 1 hour as a 'serious' level of pollution. Low concentrations of the gas cause the fine tubules of the lung to contract and this makes breathing difficult. Irritation of the upper parts of the respiratory tract occurs at higher concentrations.

Apart from the direct action of sulphur dioxide, the sulphuric and sulphurous acids associated with it present an environmental hazard. It has been shown that mist-borne sulphuric acid is more harmful to experimental animals than an equivalent concentration of sulphur dioxide. Sulphur trioxide which is quickly transformed into sulphuric acid within the lungs produces an irritation of similar magnitude to that produced by the acid mist.

Analysis of air from American cities has indicated that sulphur dioxide alone exists at undesirably high levels before taking account of the acids derived from it. Levels as high as 2·2 ppm have been recorded in cities such as Chicago and Detroit which is uncomfortably close to the 'serious' level defined by the State of California.

Oxides and acids of sulphur were implicated in the disastrous London smog of 1952. The smog was so named because it was a mixture of smoke and fog and it is estimated to have killed some 4,000 people during that winter. Many of the deaths resulted from chronic bronchitis in older people with a history of respiratory disease. It was clear that their condition was aggravated by the smog but the pollutants responsible proved hard to identify. The highest recorded level of sulphur dioxide during the smog was 1·34 ppm which is below the figures quoted for Chicago and Detroit at a time when there was no comparable problem. It does not seem likely, therefore, that the gas itself was the main cause. It is now believed that smoke and sulphuric acid mist played a more important role in this disaster than was suspected at the time. Certain synergistic effects have been demonstrated between the various components of smog which throw some light on the problem. Notwithstanding the experience in American cities, levels of sulphur dioxide as low as 0·21 ppm can have a serious effect upon victims of chronic bronchitis when in the presence of 300 $\mu g/m^3$ of smoke. Furthermore, low levels of sulphur dioxide and sulphuric acid aerosol applied simultaneously produce greater irritation than can be anticipated from their action when administered separately. These findings are an example of the complexity that can be encountered in pollution problems and illustrate the difficulty of assigning a safety level to one pollutant without regard to others.

The sensitivity of vegetation to sulphur dioxide has long been recognised and often gives an early indication of pollution. Sulphur dioxide itself tends to be more toxic to plants than sulphuric acid aerosols, which is in contrast to the situation in vertebrates. Some plants are damaged by concentrations of 0·2 ppm and above, the magnitude of the effect depending upon the period of exposure. Absorption occurs through the stomata and the gas is quickly oxidised to sulphate upon entry into cells. The toxicity of sulphur dioxide to plants is connected with its reducing action rather than its acidity.

The oxides and acids of sulphur damage metals and building materials as well as living organisms. Experiments have shown that iron rusts rapidly when in contact with air containing traces of sulphur dioxide, ash and smoke. Removal of any one of these three factors causes a sharp decline in the rate of rusting. In view of these findings, it is hardly surprising that iron rusts nearly three times as quickly in industrial Sheffield as it does in Farnborough, Hampshire. Solutions of sulphurous and sulphuric acid readily dissolve calcium carbonate, and this process contributes to the conspicuous weathering of limestone buildings in industrial towns.

Nickel and cobalt catalyse oxidation of sulphur dioxide and so develop a surface film of sulphuric acid when exposed to the gas. Sulphates are formed due to the acid attacking the metal. Similarly, copper plating becomes coated with a protective 'patina' of basic copper sulphate which gives a distinctive green colouration to copper roofs.

Generations of schoolboys have recognised the extraordinary sensitivity of the human nose to hydrogen sulphide (H_2S). Since as little as 0·1 ppm in the air is noticed by most people, early warning of pollution is assured. Nevertheless, a cautionary word is necessary. Exposure to 100 ppm for a few minutes impairs the sense of smell and continued inhalation at this concentration causes severe irritation of the respiratory tract.

A serious case of hydrogen sulphide pollution occurred in Mexico in 1950. Accidental spillage resulted in a high concentration in the air lasting for about one hour. Twenty-two people died and there were three hundred and twenty hospital cases. Those affected by the gas had lost their sense of smell.

Hydrogen sulphide produced during the processing of petroleum and in the production of coal gas and paper pulp is an important source of air pollution. Once in the air it is oxidised to sulphuric acid by oxygen, the overall reaction being:

$$H_2S + 2O_2 \rightarrow H_2SO_4$$

Thus its life in the atmosphere is transitory and perceptible concentrations are

41

seldom encountered in spite of the fact that some 300 million tons are released every year. The oxidation of hydrogen sulphide to sulphuric acid is also carried out by certain bacteria.

Hydrogen fluoride (HF) is a poisonous and highly corrosive gas which attacks glass. It dissolves in water to form hydrofluoric acid which yields fluoride ions (F⁻) upon dissociation. As an atmospheric pollutant it arises from reduction of phosphate fertilisers, smelting of iron ores, manufacture of ceramics and other industrial processes.

Both hydrogen fluoride and silicon tetrafluoride (SiF_4) are discharged into the air during industrial processes, the latter being hydrolysed by atmospheric moisture to yield hydrofluoric acid and sulphur dioxide.

$$SiF_4 + 2H_2O \rightarrow 4HF + SO_2$$

Atmospheric hydrogen fluoride dissolves in rain droplets which carry it down to the land surface.

Airborne fluoride gases are not usually at sufficiently high concentrations to affect animals directly. However, farm animals can be poisoned by fluoride residues that have been deposited from the air upon vegetation. Whilst a few parts per million of fluoride are beneficial to animals, higher levels produce symptoms of fluorosis – mottling of teeth and high density and brittleness of bones.

Certain plants, on the other hand, are extremely sensitive to fluoride gases. Gladioli, for example, show symptoms of poisoning after exposure to only 0·0001 ppm atmospheric fluoride over a period of five weeks. In plants fluoride migrates towards the leaf margins after entering through the stomata, and in the example cited the leaf concentration had reached 150 ppm in areas showing marginal necrosis. Young leaves tend to be more susceptible to fluoride poisoning than old leaves. Fluoride ions probably accumulate in plants because they are not metabolised and are but slowly removed by translocation and volatilisation.

Mean atmospheric levels of total fluoride measured in the U.S.A. range from 0·003 ppm to 0·08 ppm, rising to 0·3 ppm in the neighbourhood of superphosphate plants. Such levels do not suggest any direct effects upon animals or man but this should not encourage complacency. The ability of plants to accumulate fluoride represents a threat both to themselves and to the animals which feed upon them.

The London smog provides an example of a complex pollution problem. Of greater complexity still is the photochemical air pollution prevalent in the Los Angeles basin, sometimes rather misleadingly called 'smog'. Unlike the London version, Los Angeles 'smog' develops under clear skies where there is strong solar radiation. It is caused by the interaction of pollutants expelled in car exhausts under the influence of sunlight. The pollutants involved are gaseous oxides of nitrogen and a variety of organic substances formed during the incomplete combustion of petrol including saturated and unsaturated hydrocarbons, aromatic compounds and aldehydes. At the high temperature of the internal combustion engine nitrogen and oxygen combine to produce nitric oxide.

$$N_2 + O_2 \rightarrow 2NO$$

Subsequent rapid cooling of the exhaust gases encourages formation of nitrogen dioxide and nitrogen tetroxide according to the following equilibrium. The temperatures associated with the different equilibrium states are noted.

$$2NO + O_2 \underset{\longleftarrow}{\overset{650° \quad 150°}{\longrightarrow}} 2NO_2 \underset{\longleftarrow}{\overset{140° \quad 0°}{\longrightarrow}} N_2O_4$$

Nitrogen dioxide absorbs incoming solar radiation in the blue and near ultra violet range of the spectrum and duly splits up to form nitric oxide and atomic oxygen.

$$NO_2 + h\nu \rightarrow NO + O \; (h\nu = \text{one unit of light energy})$$

In other photochemical reactions aldehydes are split up to form free radicals and oxygen molecules are converted into activated (singlet) oxygen.

All these photochemical products are highly reactive and they initiate an extremely complicated sequence of reactions. Organic free radicals link with activated oxygen to form peroxyacyl radicals which combine in turn with nitrogen dioxide yielding peroxyacyl nitrates (notably peroxyacetyl nitrate) and other more stable compounds.

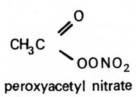

peroxyacetyl nitrate

Both peroxyacyl radicals and atomic oxygen can react with molecular oxygen to form ozone (O_3). Ozone reacts with nitric oxide to regenerate nitrogen dioxide.

All told, some 750 tons of oxides of nitrogen and 250 tons of organic substances are released per day in the Los Angeles area. The visible product of their photochemical transformation is the 'smog' which can be penetrated by sunlight but which is not necessarily dispersed by it. The windlessness and the poor ventilation favour its persistence. Plant damage is caused by it, and the symptoms produced suggest that peroxyacetyl nitrate and ozone are both involved.

So far the 'smog' has not been shown to have any serious effect upon human health. There is no evidence of increased rates of hospital admission for respiratory and cardiac diseases when it is bad. This is encouraging, but it does not rule out the possibility of chronic effects. It has been shown for example that ozone can be harmful to health in the long term. Exposure to 1 ppm for 8 hours per day over a period of a year can cause bronchitis and other diseases of the respiratory system.

Although 'smog' cannot be condemned as a health hazard on present evidence, eye irritation, reduced visibility and damage to vegetation are all undesirable consequences of it which become noticeable when the oxidants associated with it exceed 0·15 ppm in the air. This concentration has accordingly been defined as an 'adverse' level by the Department of Public Health.

Generally speaking, the gases mentioned here are only dangerous or troublesome near to their point of release. Rapid diffusion, chemical transformation and solution in rain or surface waters all contribute to a speedy decline in air concentration. Not surprisingly, pollution by gases is a problem largely restricted to urban areas. One possible exception to this is carbon dioxide. If the pessimistic view is correct, increases in the atmospheric content of this gas may trigger off far-reaching climatic changes over the next century or two.

Frequently, it is the reaction products rather than the original gases which are responsible for inimical effects. Sulphuric acid mists are more damaging to the lungs than the sulphur dioxide from which they are derived. The oxidation products of nitrogen dioxide are more troublesome than the gas itself in photochemical air pollution.

The reactivity of most polluting gases proves to be a double-edged weapon. On the one hand, it often ensures rapid removal of the gas from the air; on the other hand, it is sometimes the cause of a further pollution problem.

The limitation of gaseous pollution depends to a large extent on control of emissions from chimneys, extraction systems and car exhausts. The use of high chimneys to aid dispersal, the scrubbing of flue gases, and the employment of exhaust 'after-burners' are all ways in which the problem is being tackled. As with most other forms of pollution, the solution is to hand if society is willing to meet the cost.

IV

Heavy Metals

MINERALS containing heavy metallic elements are of widespread occurrence in rocks and soils. When they are weathered, cations of the heavy metals are liberated and find their way into surface waters and soil water. This has been happening since early geological times, and it is only within the last few hundred years that man has significantly affected their environmental levels.

Lead, copper and zinc are heavy metals that have been extensively mined, and whose environmental levels have been strongly influenced by man. All are rather toxic to living organisms and may be regarded as pollutants. In spite of this, traces of copper and zinc are essential to life. Like molybdenum, cobalt and iron, they function as co-factors for certain enzyme systems. Traces of these elements in the soil are essential for normal plant growth. A poison at relatively high concentration can turn out to be an essential co-factor at lower concentration.

Most of the following account is concerned with the ionic forms of lead, copper, zinc and nickel. Mention will also be made of organic lead, which is sometimes associated with inorganic lead in the environment. The insecticide lead arsenate and copper fungicides will be discussed here in preference to the later chapter on insecticides and fungicides.

Lead has been mined in Britain since the time of the Romans. It is a soft metal of high density with an atomic weight of 207 and is commonly encountered as the divalent plumbous ion (Pb^{2+}). Atomic lead can show some reluctance to part with its valency electrons, and by the same token, ionic lead quite readily picks up electrons. Thus lead forms covalent compounds such as tetraethyl lead ($Pb(C_2H_5)_4$) and tetrapropyl lead ($Pb(C_3H_7)_4$), illustrating its ability to share electrons rather than to lose them. Like the ions of certain other heavy metals, lead ions interact with the sulphydryl (—SH) groups of proteins, a reaction which can cause the precipitation of proteins. The most important lead ore is galena (PbS) which is characterised by its high density and its insolubility in water.

When lead finds its way into animals it tends to be laid down in bone and is only slowly excreted. Thus its action can be long-term and there is evidence that lead stored in bone is returned to the circulation during periods of illness. Where lead intake is fairly constant, plateau levels can be established.

Lead has a number of well-defined toxic effects upon man including the production of anaemia, disturbances of haemoglobin synthesis and damage to the nervous system and kidneys. When haemoglobin synthesis is inhibited, two intermediates in the process, β-amino laevulinic acid and coproporphyrin III build up and appear at abnormally high concentrations in the urine. These events can give an early warning of poisoning. It is quite likely that retarded haemoglobin production is the cause of anaemia in the presence of lead. Damage to the brain (lead encephalopathy) is a more serious consequence of lead poisoning and infants are more susceptible to it than adults, both in humans and experimental animals. Damage to the kidney (chronic nephritis) can result from long-term exposure to lead, and was shown to be an occupational hazard in the lead industry in a study conducted in the 1920's.

The acute lethal dose of inorganic lead for man has been estimated at between 300 and 700 mg/kg. The rat, however, is less sensitive and can tolerate relatively high levels over a considerable period of time.

Pb^{2+} is also quite toxic to fish, and it has been shown that concentrations as low as 0·33 ppm in water can be lethal to certain species (Table 4.1). Like Cu^{2+} and Zn^{2+}, it is less toxic in hard waters than in soft waters because its toxicity is antagonised by ions such as Ca^{2+} and Mg^{2+}.

Turning now to the environment, appreciable quantities of lead are found in soils. Some of this is derived from soil minerals, whilst other sources include deposition from the air, deliberate application for pest control and dumped materials containing the element. The relative importance of these different sources varies from area to area. In mining districts, the weathering of lead minerals makes a substantial contribution to the level of the element in soils. Near major highways airborne lead derived from car exhausts is of major importance, whilst in some orchards considerable quantities reach the soil following the use of lead arsenate as an insecticide. In general, lead applied to the soil is strongly retained in the top few inches, and is only slowly carried down by leaching presumably due to its interaction with soil colloids. It is therefore liable to be quite peristent in soils.

Since lead is widely used in industry it is liable to be well represented in rubbish dumps and this can be the cause of local soil pollution. The real danger of this was illustrated by a case of lead poisoning in children which was traced to the consumption of lettuces containing high levels of the element. The source of lead proved to be old lead batteries dumped on the ground in the neighbourhood of vegetable plots.

As we have seen, soil lead levels are usually high in old mining areas where it often occurs in association with significant amounts of zinc, nickel and copper. The presence of high levels of these metals in soils can have interesting effects upon the flora.

Table 4.1. Lowest concentrations of heavy metals in water shown
to cause fish mortalities,
within stated times

Metal	Salt	Concentration of metal (ppm) and time of exposure (hr)	
		Stickleback	Rainbow Trout
Copper	$Cu(NO_3)_2$	0·02 (192 hr)	0·08 (20 hr)
Lead	$Pb(NO_3)_2$	0·33 (? hr)	1·0 (100 hr)
Zinc	$ZnSO_4$	0·3 (204 hr)	0·5 (64 hr)
Nickel	$Ni(NO_3)_2$	1·0 (156 hr)	—

Although lead concentrations exceeding 10 ppm in soil are normally toxic to plants, certain strains that can tolerate them exist in old mining areas. Specimens of the grass, *Agrostis tenuis*, taken from such sites show resistance not only to lead, but also to copper, zinc and nickel. Resistance is confined to the strains found in mining areas and is not shared by members of the same species in other localities. Although tolerance to lead is often associated with tolerance to other heavy metals, this is not invariably the case. Lead tolerance alone can be developed in some plants and it would therefore appear to be mediated by a specific mechanism not directly concerned with resistance to other ions.

There has been speculation about the length of time necessary for resistant strains to evolve. The problem might be a relatively simple one if it could be assumed that their evolution started with the commencement of mining operations. However, soil lead levels tend to be high in areas rich in lead minerals whether there is mining or not; mining merely causes the elevation of a concentration that is already relatively high. Therefore it is probable that natural selection for resistant strains commenced long before the intervention of man in these mining areas.

Pb^{2+} is also a pollutant of surface waters. However, only relatively small quantities reach water via the air or in drainage water and run-off from agricultural land. Industrial effluents, notably those arising from lead mines are the most important sources of lead in rivers. Galena is an important source of the lead in surface waters. Although extremely insoluble it is slowly oxidised by air into the somewhat more water soluble sulphate.

$$PbS + 2\,O_2 \to PbSO_4$$

Lead sulphate and certain other lead salts formed by weathering of minerals dissolve in water to yield the toxic Pb^{2+} ion which is carried into rivers and streams, sometimes with severe consequences. There have been rivers and streams in Welsh mining areas completely devoid of rooted plants due to high Pb^{2+} concentrations. In extreme cases where the Pb^{2+} concentration has reached 0·5 ppm, flora and fauna have been limited to the algae *Batrachospermum* and *Sacheria* and a few insects. With the decline of lead mining since the turn of the century there has been a reduction in the lead content of affected rivers and a corresponding improvement in fauna and flora.

River pollutants like lead are most concentrated in the neighbourhood of outfalls. As we have seen, the concentration declines rapidly further downstream as a consequence of dilution, chemical change and precipitation, and the concentration gradient may be accompanied by a corresponding gradient of the flora and fauna. Reduction of Pb^{2+} concentrations in Welsh rivers has been accomplished by running outfalls from mine workings through beds of limestone chips.

The tendency of lead to accumulate in animals has raised questions about human health hazards. Most reported cases of lead poisoning in adults have been due to occupational exposure, whilst most of those in children and farm animals have been regarded as accidental, often due to the consumption of lead paints. Such localised instances of poisoning are not relevant here except in so far as they have been given information on toxicity. It is the question of man's exposure to environmental lead that now demands attention.

Lead is absorbed by humans in two distinct ways – from the alimentary tract and through the lungs. Surveys conducted in the U.S.A. have measured human lead absorption, and their principle findings are summarised in Table 4.2. The figures are for total lead and therefore include some organic lead. Similar results have been obtained in British surveys. It will be seen that the principal sources of lead are food, urban air and tobacco smoke. It appears that only a small proportion of this lead is naturally derived.

Water is only a minor source contributing 10 mg per day of which only 10 per cent is absorbed. However, these are average figures and levels in tap water are locally high where lead pipes are in use. Absorption is more efficient via the lungs than via the alimentary tract, and although urban non-smokers take twelve times as much lead into the gut as they do into the lungs, only twice as much is actually absorbed by this route. The high intake of lead by smokers may not simply be due to absorption of the element in tobacco smoke. Nicotine in the tobacco apparently increases the efficiency with which smokers absorb lead already in the air.

Table 4.2. Average daily intake of lead by a 'normal' person in the U.S.A.

Substance	Daily Intake	Lead Concentration In Substance	Lead Ingested Per Day (mg)	Fraction Absorbed	Lead Absorbed Per Day (mg)
Food	2 kg	0·17 ppm	330	0·05	17
Water	1 kg	0·01 ppm	10	0·1	1
Urban Air	20 cubic metres (m³)	1·3 mg/m³*	26	0·4	10·4
Rural Air	20 cubic metres (m³)	0·05mg/m³*	1	0·4	0·4
Tobacco Smoke	30 cigarettes	0·8 mg per cigarette	24	0·4	9·6

* Much of this is in the form of lead chloride and lead oxide

Dietary lead originates from many sources including lead solder, lead paint, lead pipes, car exhausts and lead arsenate insecticide. Much of the lead in urban air, however, is derived from a single source – car exhausts. It is added to petrol in the form of tetraethyl lead $(Pb(C_2H_5)_4)$ and other lead tetra alkyls to raise the octane number; i.e. it helps to eliminate knock or semi-explosive burning, an improvement that can also be achieved by further refining of the petrol. During the operation of an internal combustion engine most of the tetra alkyl lead is broken down to inorganic lead which is released with the exhaust gases. An apparently small but as yet undetermined quantity of tetra alkyl lead is emitted with exhaust gases, and is included in the figure for total atmospheric lead given in Table 4.2.

Since lead tetra alkyls are volatile they can get into the air when petrol evaporates. This is obviously a problem with petrol spillage in enclosed spaces such as garages, but the contribution made to environmental lead is probably small. Other sources of airborne inorganic lead include lead paints and lead arsenate insecticide.

Attempts have been made to assess man's increasing exposure to atmospheric lead by studying levels of the element in snow in the Greenland Ice Sheet. The date of deposition of snow taken at different depths from the surface can be assessed with reasonable accuracy, so lead levels in different samples can give some idea of atmospheric contamination during certain periods. These studies indicate that there was a fourfold increase in atmospheric lead between 1750 and 1950, and a sharper increase between 1950 and the mid-1960's. This parallels the increased use of lead over this period in the Northern hemisphere. Snow samples from the Antarctic do not show this increase but this is not surprising since the Southern hemisphere has no comparable history of lead usage and not much atmospheric contamination is to be expected.

In attempting to assess the health hazard presented by environmental lead, surveys have been conducted on blood lead levels. A survey in the U.S.A. reported that normal blood levels were in the range 0·15–0·70 ppm by weight, and averaged 0·3 ppm. These are disquietingly close to the threshold value of 0·8 ppm accepted by many workers as the level above which symptoms of poisoning begin to show. Indeed, some authorities cite cases of lead poisoning in children with blood levels below 0·4 ppm, although the accuracy of analysis is in some doubt. However, blood lead levels are not very closely correlated with symptoms of poisoning. One complicating factor is that blood lead is almost entirely carried by red cells. Where individuals have low red cell counts they have a correspondingly poor capacity for carrying lead in the blood. Thus a relatively low concentration in an anaemic person may be more serious than a higher concentration in another person with a high red-cell count; the red cells may be carrying a higher concentration in the anaemic person. It might be easier to relate blood lead levels to toxic effect if they were expressed in terms of red-cell weight instead of total blood weight.

Another line of approach has involved the study of industrial workers with occupational exposure to much higher lead levels than the general population. So far, results from this work have been encouraging. No serious effects on health have been observed even with exposure over a period of years. However, this work is of limited usefulness. It is desirable to have data for even longer periods of time with larger numbers of experimental subjects, taking into account any local factors that may influence susceptibility to lead poisoning, e.g. exposure to other chemicals. Again these findings are for adults and there are no comparable studies for children, an unsatisfactory state of affairs since children react differently from older people, showing greater susceptibility and some differences in symptoms. The situation is complex and it seems unlikely that all the answers can ever be known.

The foregoing remarks refer mainly to inorganic lead. Organic lead poses special problems and has been less well investigated. Tetraethyl lead, the most commonly encountered of the tetra alkyl lead compounds, is a volatile, fat soluble liquid used as an anti-knock in petrol. It is slowly metabolised to the triethyl lead ion within the body, notably by the liver, and this is more toxic to vertebrates than the parent compound. Owing to its fat

$$Pb (C_2H_5)_4 \rightarrow Pb (C_2H_5)_3{}^+$$

Tetraethyl lead   Triethyl lead ion

solubility lead tetraethyl readily crosses the blood-brain barrier and encephalopathy can result from a few ppm of the poison in the brain. In mild cases of poisoning the symptoms include insomnia, restlessness, loss of appetite and gastro-intestinal disturbances. In fatal cases, delirium, hallucinations, convulsions and coma precede death. Thus it differs from inorganic lead in that its action is predominantly on the central nervous system, and it does not necessarily produce certain of the classical symptoms of inorganic lead poisoning, e.g. elevated excretion of coproporphyrin III.

Tetraethyl lead was introduced as a petrol additive in 1923, and from the first it was viewed with apprehension. A number of deaths and cases of non-lethal intoxication resulted from occupational exposure to the compound and led to the formulation of safety regulations in the U.S.A. Since their introduction in 1926, 88 cases of poisoning have been reported in the U.S.A. and Canada, 16 of them fatal.

Regarding air pollution, tetraethyl lead has received most attention as the source of inorganic lead in car exhausts. Up till now the contribution of the organic compound itself to atmospheric lead has not been properly determined. Neither has it been distinguished from the inorganic element in measuring human blood levels. The quantity absorbed by humans is unknown, in spite of its disturbing toxicological properties.

Copper is a metal with an old and interesting history. Under the Pharaohs, copper smelting was an important industry. Bronze is an alloy of copper which gave its name to an early cultural age. Copper is of wide distribution in nature and in the works of man. It is described as a noble metal because it is rather stable in the elemental state and is reluctant to lose electrons and pass into the ionic state. It is also a transition element and shows the typical features of variable valency, coloured ions, and a tendency towards complex formation. Cu^{2+} forms stable complexes such as chelates with organic substances and this can cause its effective removal from solution. Two ionic forms are recognised – Cu^{2+} (cupric) and Cu^+ (cuprous) – the divalent form being much the more common. The principal ores are $CuFeS_2$ (copper pyrites); Cu_2S (chalcocite), CuS (indigo copper) and $Cu_5 FeS_4$ (bornite).

Copper is an essential constituent of living systems. Ionic copper is a co-factor for certain enzyme systems mediating redox reactions.

Cu^{2+} is toxic to most forms of life, 0·5 ppm in water being lethal to many algae, whilst most fish succumb to a few parts per million. As little as 0·02 ppm of the element is lethal to the stickleback over a period of 8 days (Table 4.1). In higher animals brain damage is a characteristic feature of copper poisoning. The reason for its high toxicity is still controversial although there is evidence that it can inhibit certain enzymes by affecting their sulphydryl groups.

Man has influenced environmental levels of copper ever since he began to mine the element. Nowadays, copper pollution may arise from many sources. Soils receive high levels as the result of mining activities or the application of copper fungicides, whilst effluents from factories and mines sometimes cause serious river pollution.

Copper has a dualistic action in the soil – as an essential plant nutrient and as a wide spectrum poison. Copper deficiency in plants has been encountered on sandy and gravelly soils in Australia and South Africa and on reclaimed peats in Europe and the U.S.A. Deficiency can be a question of low availability rather than absence of the element from the soil. Cu^{2+} is strongly complexed by soil organic matter, and when in this form it is not readily available to plants.

At the same time, strong binding can contribute to build-up over a long period when regular additions are made to the soil. The accumulation of copper in soils has given rise to concern in the neighbourhood of mine workings and on agricultural and horticultural sites receiving large doses of copper fungicides.

Soils in some old mining areas contain levels of Cu^{2+} that would normally be toxic to plants. As with lead, however, *Agrostis tenuis* and other species are represented in such localities by resistant strains. Cu^{2+} tolerance can be developed independently of that towards other metals.

Some agricultural soils receive much copper in the form of the fungicides copper oxychloride ($CuCl_2.\ 3\ Cu(OH)_2$)* and bordeaux mixture ($CuSO_4.\ 3\ Cu(OH)_2$)* used as fungicides. These compounds are of very low solubility in water and so do not release significant amounts of Cu^{2+} under normal conditions. On account of this, they are safe to apply to plant leaves which are highly sensitive to the ion. Fungal spores, on the other hand, exude substances that can solubilise copper from the fungicidal deposit; the organic complex so formed finds its way into the spore with fatal consequences.

Intensive use of copper fungicides in some English orchards has had serious consequences. Cases have been reported of the metal reaching a level of 0·2 per cent in the surface litter, and of the underlying soil becoming almost totally devoid of animal life including earthworms (*Lumbricus terrestris*). Earthworms were apparently poisoned after ingestion of surface leaf litter high in copper. Following the disappearance of earthworms the different layers of the orchard soil were not properly mixed.

Once copper fungicide reaches the soil, slow release of Cu^{2+} may be anticipated. Unfortunately the significance of this does not appear to have been properly investigated.

* Tentative formulae

Some industrial effluents from copper-plating works are rich in Cu^{2+} and can cause serious river pollution. Levels as high as 1·6 ppm were recorded below copper works on the river Churnet in 1938. For several miles downstream from the point of discharge no animals were found and the numbers of algae were severely reduced. Near the outfall only *Chlorococcum spp* and *Achnathes affinis* were found but further downstream other species reappeared in great numbers. This abnormally large algal population was apparently due to the absence of 'grazing' pressure from the fauna which was very sensitive to copper poisoning (note Figure 1.1).

In conclusion, it should be emphasised that toxicity resides in Cu^{2+} rather than in covalently combined copper. Thus bordeaux mixture and copper oxychloride, and organic complexes in soil or water, are only reservoirs of the toxic ion and express little toxicity in their own right.

Zinc shows more tendency than copper to lose electrons and is commonly encountered as Zn^{2+}. Unlike copper, it does not show variable valency; neither does it readily enter into complex formation. The principal ores are zinc blende (ZnS) and Smithsonite ($ZnCO_3$). Zinc blende is insoluble in water but is oxidised to soluble zinc sulphate during weathering.

$$ZnS + 2\ O_2 \rightarrow ZnSO_4$$

Zn^{2+} ions are sometimes washed out of mining sites in fair concentration because of this reaction.

Toxicity is extremely variable between species. In water, concentrations of as little as 0·3 ppm are lethal to some snails and fish (Table 4.1), whereas water boatmen, stone flies and caddis worms can tolerate 500 ppm. A concentration of 7 ppm in soil retards plant growth.

Zn^{2+} tolerant strains of *Agrostis tenuis* occur in Welsh mining areas. By contrast with tolerance to Pb^{2+} and Cu^{2+}, Zn^{2+} tolerance is not developed independently, for the strains in question also tolerate Ni^{2+} where they have not been exposed to levels of this ion that are normally toxic.

Zn^{2+} is a common pollutant of fresh water, often in association with other heavy metal ions such as Pb^{2+}. The effects of zinc effluents in fresh water are influenced by a number of factors. With rainbow trout Zn^{2+} is much more toxic in soft waters of pH 6·6–6·7 than in hard waters of pH 7·6–7·8. Toxicity can also be temperature dependent, tending to increase with rising temperature in the range 15·5–21·5°C. In common with Pb^{2+} and Cu^{2+}, Zn^{2+} toxicity to fish is increased when the dissolved oxygen concentration is lowered. This is because more water must be pumped past the gills to meet oxygen requirements, thereby increasing both the circulation and the uptake of the ion.

To summarise, the heavy metals, lead, copper and zinc, have a number of features in common. They all form ions, and it is these rather than the original metals that are toxic and present pollution problems. All of the metals are economically important and have been mined over a considerable period of human history. Serious pollution of rivers and streams can originate from industrial effluents and mine workings, whilst abnormally high soil concentrations are common in mining areas. Tolerant strains of certain plants are found in these contaminated soils. In the pollution of rivers and soils several heavy metals often occur together in relatively large amounts. Sometimes the effects of the individual ions are additive but they do not always operate independently of one another. As we have seen, Zn^{2+} and Ni^{2+} tolerances are related in *Agrostis tenuis* – exposure to one ion leads to development of resistance to both. Again, Ni^{2+} and Zn^{2+}, and Cu^{2+} and Zn^{2+} show synergistic effects in the poisoning of fish. The toxicity of the two ions supplied together is greater than the summation of their individual effects.

Unlike most organic pollutants, metal ions cannot be broken down into inert substances so they can persist indefinitely in the environment. On the other hand, dilution and precipitation quickly reduce their concentrations in waterways whilst they can be inactivated in soils by complexing with organic substances.

Of the heavy metals discussed here, lead has caused most concern as a general environmental pollutant. In urban areas nearly as much lead is absorbed into the body from the air as from food and water. Lead paint, lead pipes, lead arsenate insecticide and mined lead ores have all been sources of the element in the general environment. Lead tetra alkyls are widely used as anti-knock agents in petrols and are a major source of atmospheric lead.

Inorganic lead accumulates in vertebrate bone whilst organic lead is stored in fatty tissue, and the toxicology of the two forms of the element also differs in other important respects. In view of its widespread distribution and its known toxic properties much more needs to be done on the environmental hazards presented by this element. Some of the issues involved in control of lead pollution will be discussed in Chapter VII.

V

Insecticides and Fungicides

INSECTICIDES and fungicides contrast with most other pollutants in one important respect. They are deliberately released into the environment as sprays, dusts and granules, to control pests and diseases, and are not simply undesirable waste products presenting disposal problems. Whereas many other pollutants are only important in the urban setting, pesticides are pre-eminently a problem of the field. At first sight, they seem comfortably remote from most human beings so long as there is effective control of their residues in agricultural produce. Unlike sulphur dioxide and carbon monoxide they are not released in the vicinity of large numbers of people.

Unfortunately there are complications. The strong persistence of some pesticides in the inorganic environment and, more ominously, in living organisms has given rise to unforeseen side effects. For example, levels of organochlorine insecticides have been reported in fish that have rendered them unsafe for human consumption in the view of health authorities.

The side effects of persistent agricultural poisons have made very good news, and the press has not always presented the case in an objective way. Nevertheless, publicity has helped to stimulate research on the harmful effects of insecticides and fungicides. It is to be hoped that this will be of value not only in assessing compounds presently in use but also in anticipating future events.

The insecticides that have caused most concern as pollutants are synthetic organic compounds which have only come into use during and since the 1939–45 war. Before this time, naturally occurring substances such as pyrethrum, nicotine and rotenone were the principal insecticides. Since 1940 two important groups of synthetic insecticides have emerged – the organochlorine compounds and the organophosphorus esters (organophosphates). Together they account for the greater part of the present world production of insecticides.

Although both groups of insecticides can affect the nervous system they do so in different ways. The organophosphates or their metabolites have this action because they are powerful inhibitors of the enzyme acetylcholinesterase.* The organochlorine insecticides do not inhibit this enzyme but can affect the nervous system by moving into the nerve membrane. The organochlorine insecticides are solids of extremly low water solubility, whilst the organophosphates are liquids often of appreciable water solubility. Generally speaking, the organophosphates are rapidly metabolised and excreted by animals. By contrast, certain organochlorine compounds or their metabolites are resistant to breakdown and are highly persistent within animals.

Due to the ease with which organophosphates are metabolised, they tend not to be very persistent in the living environment. Their environmental effects are liable to be immediate and reasonably predictable. It is the persistent organochlorine insecticides which have come under fire as environmental pollutants, and the rest of this account will be devoted to them.

pṕ DDT (*pp*-dichlorophenyl trichloroethane) was first synthesised in the nineteenth century, but its insecticidal properties were not recognised until the time of the last war. The discovery was made by the Swiss firm of Geigy who passed the information on to the British and American Governments. In due course DDT was used for vector control during the war, and came to be widely employed in industry medicine, and the household in the post-war years.

Technical DDT which is used in the preparation of commercial formulations is a mixture of compounds. Its main components are *pṕ* DDT (70–80 per cent), *oṕ* DDT (15–20 per cent) and *pṕ* DDD, also known as *pṕ* TDE (1–4 per cent). *pṕ* DDT accounts for most of the insecticidal activity although *pṕ* DDD (henceforward referred to as DDD) is quite toxic to some species and is used as an insecticide in its own right.

pṕ DDT is a stable solid which is very insoluble in water (<0·01 ppm) but appreciably soluble in oils and many organic solvents. It has a low vapour pressure and only volatilises slowly when exposed to air.

In view of its marked biological persistence, considerable interest has centred on the fate of *pṕ* DDT within animals (Figure 5.1). It is slowly metabolised to *pṕ* DDE (henceforward referred to as DDE) by the removal of HCl from the molecule. *pṕ* DDT is also broken down anaerobically to DDD, by certain micro-organisms and post mortem by vertebrate tissues such as liver and muscle. This raises problems of interpretation, as DDD residues may be derived from three sources – DDD in technical DDT, DDD (Rhothane) insecticides, or *pṕ* DDT residues in tissues or microorganisms. *pṕ* DDT is also hydroxylated to kelthane by some insects.

* They appear to affect the invertebrate nervous system in a similar way

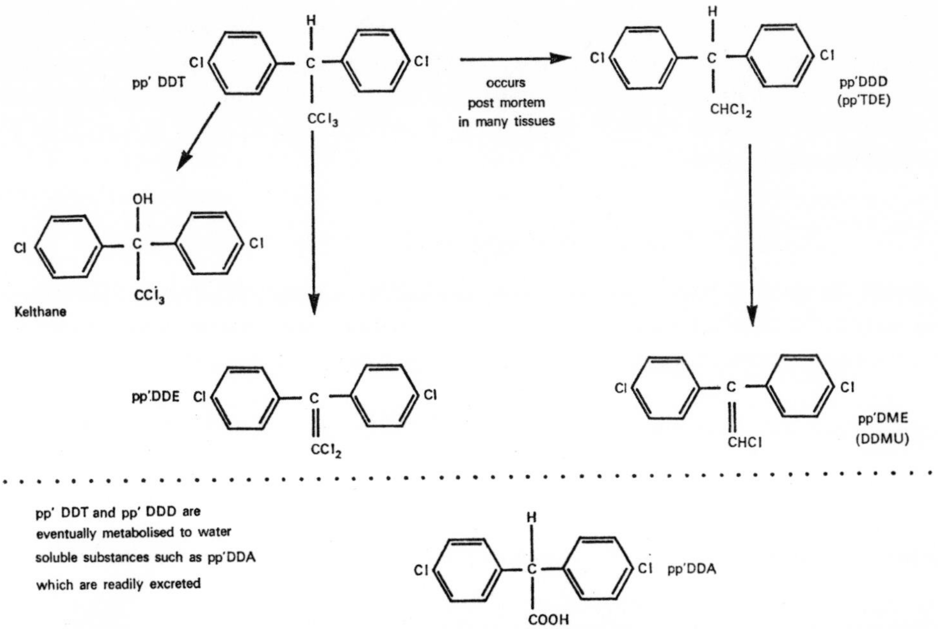

Fig. 5.1 Metabolism of *pṗ* DDT

Like *pṗ* DDT, the metabolites DDE and DDD are fat soluble and are only slowly broken down and excreted by animals. Not many measurements of their half lives have been made but the values for the pigeon should give some idea of the time scale involved (Table 5.1).

Table 5.1. Half lives of organochlorine compounds

Half Lives of *pp* DDT and two of its metabolites in the pigeon	
pp DDT	28 days
pp DDD	24 days
pp DDE	250 days
Half Lives of Dieldrin	
Male rat	12–15 days
Pigeon	47 days (mean)
Dog	28–42 days
Human	369 days (mean)

The very long half life for DDE is not altogether surprising, for it is the most widespread and abundant of all organochlorine insecticide residues found in wild

57

vertebrates. Comparison of the half life for pp DDT with the time taken for 50 per cent disappearance from soil illustrates the difference which can exist between biological and general environmental persistence (Table 5.2). The final elimination of pp DDT from the body is primarily in the form of water soluble metabolites such as pp DDA (Figure 5.1).

Table 5.2. Persistence of organochlorine insecticides in soils

Since the rate of loss from soils falls into different phases (Figure 1.5) true half lives cannot be determined. However, estimates have been made of the time taken for a particular percentage of an applied dose to disappear.

Compound	Time for 50% Loss in Years	Time for 95% Loss in Years
Dieldrin	$\frac{1}{2}$–4	4–30
pp DDT	$2\frac{1}{2}$–5	5–25
Lindane (γBHC)	(approx.) $1\frac{1}{2}$	3–10

Some figures for DDT toxicity are given in Table 5.3. The toxic action appears to be the result of its effect on the nervous system. The passage of impulses along nerves is connected with the movement of sodium and potassium ions across the nerve membrane. DDT disturbs the movement of sodium ions, and can cause nerves to behave abnormally. Whereas a normal nerve can be stimulated to produce only one impulse, a DDT-poisoned nerve will yield a series of impulses under the same conditions.

Table 5.3. The toxicity of organochlorine insecticides

Compound	Acute Oral LD_{50} mg/kg			LC_{50} (ppm) in 96 hr	
	Rat	Rabbit	Avian species	Rainbow trout	Goldfish
γBHC	200	60–200	—	0·038	0·15
DDT	150–400	250–400	>500 in most cases	0·042	0·027
Dieldrin	40–50	50–80	Pigeon 67	0·001	0·037

DDT poisoning is usually characterised by unco-ordinated twitches and tremors indicating action upon the peripheral rather than the central nervous system. pp DDT, DDE and DDD all tend to be stored in depot fats and symptoms of poisoning can be brought on when the fat is rapidly mobilised. For example, experimental birds containing these substances in their fat depots can develop symptoms during periods without food. Such latent toxicity may be important in the field and will be discussed further in connection with dieldrin.

The widespread usage of DDT makes it very difficult to be sure of the origin of its residues in the environment. In agriculture, DDT is applied as a spray or a dust or occasionally as a smoke. Since it is impossible to dissolve sufficient DDT in water to produce an effective concentration for spraying, special formulations are made which can be dispersed in water. These are either solutions of DDT in an oily liquid (emulsifiable concentrates) or fine particles of the insecticides mixed with an inert solid (wettable powders).

DDT preparations are used for such purposes as the control of biting insects on crops, ectoparasites on human beings and farm animals, insect vectors in lakes and rivers, moths in fabrics and flies inside houses. Although the insecticide inevitably reaches soils, it is not employed as a soil insecticide.

The chlorinated cyclodiene insecticides, aldrin, dieldrin and heptachlor, have a number of features in common with DDT. They too are stable solids of low water solubility and considerable fat solubility. Their metabolism is summarised in Figure 5.2 where it will be seen that aldrin is converted to dieldrin and heptachlor to heptachlor epoxide. Both processes are epoxidations which can be carried out by microsomal oxidases. The transformations are rapid and the metabolites are fat

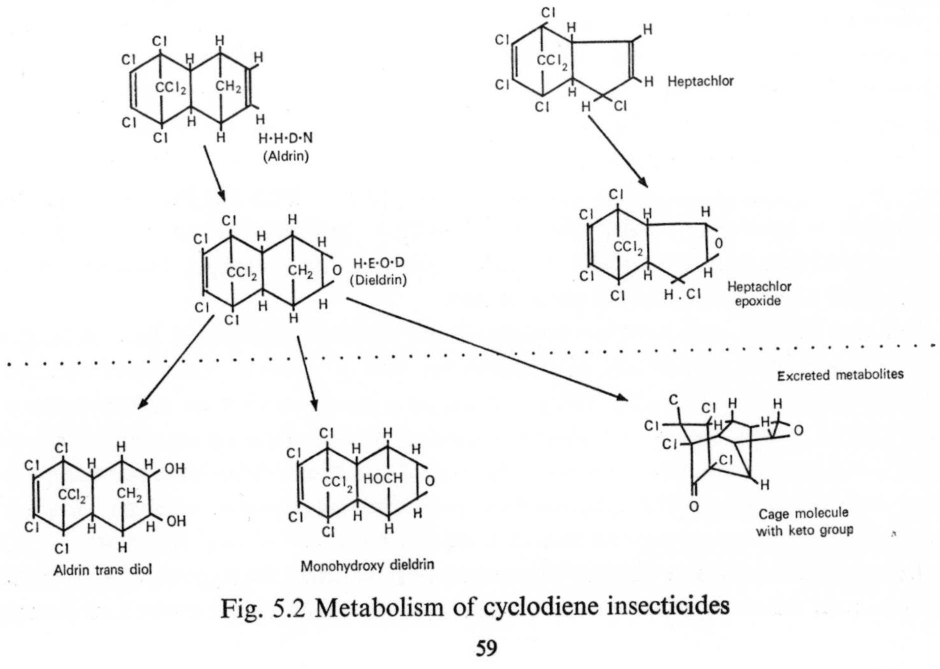

Fig. 5.2 Metabolism of cyclodiene insecticides

soluble and biologically persistent. Some half lives for dieldrin are presented in Table 5.1.

The figures show how variable the rate of disappearance can be between species and illustrate the problems that can arise when an animal like the rat is regarded as a typical experimental animal. It will be noted that the half life for humans is 30 times greater than that for the male rat. In pigeons, dieldrin proves to be twice as persistent as $p\acute{p}$ DDT or DDD but very much less persistent than DDE. Heptachlor epoxide is also known to be biologically persistent, but data on half lives is lacking.

It is very probable that these differences in persistence are mainly the consequence of variations in metabolic capacity. Although evidence is scanty, there are indications of inter-specific differences in dieldrin metabolism. The rabbit, for example, eliminates much of its dieldrin as a diol, but this metabolite is not so important in the rat (Figure 5.2). The principal metabolites identified in the rat are oxidation products (probably of the microsomal oxidases) whereas the diol is formed by a non-oxidative process.

Reference to Table 5.3 shows that dieldrin is considerably more toxic than DDT to the rat and rabbit. There is a similarity between LD_{50} values for aldrin and dieldrin which is not altogether surprising since the former is quickly transformed to the latter. Dieldrin, like DDT, produces effects upon the nervous system although the symptomatology is somewhat different. Whereas unco-ordinated twitching and tremoring is a common feature of DDT poisoning, it is seldom a response to dieldrin. Dieldrin poisoning is usually accompanied by violent convulsions suggesting an effect on the central rather than the peripheral nervous system. Carcasses are found to be in a wasted condition with little or no depot fat after death due to dieldrin or DDT poisoning. Thus mobilisation of fats seems to be an outcome of severe poisoning and can only worsen the situation by putting stored insecticide into circulation.

The uses of aldrin and dieldrin have been severely restricted in Great Britain since 1961 whilst heptachlor has completely disappeared from the market. In particular dieldrin is no longer used in sheep dips whilst the use of aldrin and dieldrin for dressing seed has been drastically curtailed. Many other countries, however, do not have similar arrangements at the present time.

For this reason, and because residues from earlier applications have a long life in the environment, the effects of dieldrin are still of interest. Currently dieldrin is still used on a small scale as a foliage spray, as a seed dressing on certain approved crops and as a root dip, whilst aldrin is used as a seed dressing on approved crops and as a soil insecticide. On the whole, the cyclodiene insecticides have been employed rather less widely than DDT, heptachlor providing an extreme example of a compound with only one approved use in Great Britain – as a seed dressing.

Benzene hexachloride (BHC) deserves brief mention as it contrasts in certain respects with other organochlorine insecticides. It exists in a number of isomeric forms of which the γ isomer (γBHC or Lindane) is the most insecticidal and the form normally encountered in commercial formulations. γBHC is considerably more water soluble (10 ppm) than $p\acute{p}$ DDT, DDD, aldrin or dieldrin. It is also metabolised quite rapidly by most living organisms. This may be because its slight water solubility does not favour storage in depot fats to the same extent as other organochlorine insecticides, i.e. it may be more available to the systems that can metabolise it. Be this as it may, γBHC is eliminated quite rapidly by vertebrates and does not persist very strongly in the living environment although it is quite long-lasting in soils.

γBHC is another nerve poison which shows a similar order of toxicity to DDT in some experimental animals (Table 5.3). It is still widely used in Britain as a foliage spray, a seed dressing and a root dip.

The combination of long persistence and appreciable toxicity that is displayed by dieldrin, heptachlor epoxide and to some extent by $p\acute{p}$ DDT and DDE has important implications with regard to their effects in the environment. These compounds will now be considered from two points of view – their distribution throughout the environment and their significance in terms of individuals and populations. The topics will be dealt with in the order given.

The introduction of gas chromatography for residue analysis made it possible to detect and determine concentrations of organochlorine insecticides as small as 0·01 ppm in animal tissues, and even lower than this in air, water and soil. Spurred on by Rachel Carson's *Silent Spring* and growing public anxiety about pollution, residue analysts have carried out a large number of surveys since 1960.

It has been found that dieldrin, DDE and $p\acute{p}$ DDT are widely distributed throughout the environment albeit in small quantities; air, rain water, soil, river water and even antarctic ice contain traces of them (Table 5.4). Indeed, it is extremely difficult to find a completely uncontaminated sample of anything at the present time. One exception to this has been old polar ice deposited before DDT came into use. Biological specimens generally carry higher organochlorine residue levels than do inorganic

Table 5.4. Organochlorine residues in soils, air, rain water and antarctic snow
(Values in parts per million million by weight)

Sample	γBHC	$p\acute{p}$ DDT	Dieldrin
London air 1965	7	3	20
London rain water 1965	20–155	70–400	10–95
British arable soils		$50–1000 \times 10^3$	$30–700 \times 10^3$
British orchard soils		$3\cdot6–26\cdot6 \times 10^6$	
Antarctic snow		40	

samples, and the finding of a blank sample has proved especially difficult. An ingenious solution to this problem came from workers in the Antarctic when they removed a fat sample from a stuffed penguin which had been left there by the Scott expedition in 1911. After careful analysis this specimen was pronounced pesticide-free.

The levels found in agricultural soils result in the main from direct applications of one kind or another, although small quantities must have been brought in by rain water. In this context the term 'direct application' may be a little misleading, for spray drift ensures that much material does not reach its intended destination. Rarely can more than 50 per cent of a sprayed pesticide be accounted for in a treated area. In an experiment with DDT in the U.S.A., only 20–30 per cent of spray chemical was trapped 8 feet above the soil surface at the time of application. Analysis of plant and soil one day later only accounted for some 10 per cent of the original material. Since DDT is known to be stable and persistent, it may be assumed that much of the unrecovered chemical was not broken down, but escaped into the air.

This raises the question of the contribution of spray drift to general rather than local air pollution. Traces of organochlorine compounds have been found in air samples taken from both urban and rural areas of Britain, and these cannot be put down to spray drift over a short distance. It has already been pointed out that fine spray droplets can travel over considerable distances. Furthermore, the organochlorine compounds have small vapour pressures, and may volatilise to some extent from airborne spray droplets. Thus, it is probable that agricultural sprays contribute to the widespread air pollution by these persistent substances. Other likely sources include material volatilising from the soil and vegetation, agricultural dusts and air extracted from factories manufacturing pesticides.

The sources of organochlorine pollution in rivers are more easily recognised. In the first place, the movement of the pesticides is more restricted and it is usually possible to trace the point of discharge of an effluent. Secondly, fish are very sensitive indicators of pollution and fish kills quickly draw attention to the problem, as was the case in the serious Rhine pollution of 1969 involving endosulfan. Although residues in rain water and run-off from agricultural land contribute to the pollution of rivers by organochlorine pesticides, the discharge of sheep dips and industrial effluents appear to have been more important factors in Britain. Some sheep farmers have discharged their dieldrin, DDT and BHC dips into the nearest rivers or streams, causing heavy fish mortality. Factories using dieldrin and DDT for mothproofing have run effluents containing these organochlorine insecticides into rivers such as the Tweed. It is not surprising then that British rivers have varied considerably in their organochlorine insecticide levels, since these tend to be a reflection of local activity rather than of general aerial pollution.

We have already had occasion to mention the danger of accumulation in lakes and seas. The high levels of DDT and its metabolites in Baltic fish, the levels of DDE and dieldrin in fish caught off the British east coast and the pollution of Loch Leven all bear witness to this. The future pollution hazards in land-locked seas such as the Black Sea and the Caspian Sea deserve serious consideration.

Turning now to soils, $p\acute{p}$ DDT, dieldrin and γBHC (Table 5.2) all show strong persistence. Volatilisation as well as microbial breakdown appears to be important in their elimination from soils. As these insoluble insecticides are adsorbed by colloids, it is not surprising that persistence tends to be strongest in soils high in organic matter. Adsorbed insecticide can be displaced to some extent by water, and this encourages volatilisation and microbial attack. Thus speed of elimination can be increased when the soil water content is raised. Extreme insolubility in water and adsorption by colloids are factors that minimise leaching of organochlorine insecticides through soil. Contamination of drainage water from agricultural land by leached organochlorine insecticides is not a problem.

The widespread dissemination of residues of organochlorine insecticides and their stable metabolites in the living environment is to be anticipated from that is known of their biological persistence. Of the compounds that have been widely used, aldrin and heptachlor are rapidly converted into dieldrin and heptachlor epoxide in living animals, and it is the stable metabolites rather than the original insecticides that appear as residues in the tissues. Similarly, $p\acute{p}$ DDT is metabolised into its more stable metabolite, DDE, which is important as a residue. Surveys of organochlorine insecticide residues in British birds and their eggs were conducted between 1960 and 1965 and some of the results are summarised in Figure 5.3. Nearly all the samples analysed contained detectable quantities of DDE and dieldrin, the highest concentration being found in body fat from carcasses and in yolk from eggs. Heptachlor epoxide, $p\acute{p}$ DDT and DDD were also found in a number of cases. In both aquatic and terrestrial habitats, predatory species contained higher average concentrations of these substances than either omnivores or herbivores. This general trend is not explicable on the grounds of differences in habitat leading to differences in exposure because studies in closely defined areas have pointed to the same conclusion. Figure 5.4 shows how DDE and dieldrin are distributed throughout the marine ecosystem in the neighbourhood of the Farne Islands. Different species have been ascribed to appropriate 'trophic levels' which are detailed in the figure. Predators are found in the highest trophic levels, and it will be seen that they contain the highest concentrations of DDE and dieldrin. There is a regular increase of concentration for both compounds moving from the lowest to the highest trophic level.

What is the reason for this correlation between residue levels and diet? The simplest explanation is that organisms in a food chain can amplify the concentration in their diets by building up the concentration of ingested substances within the body until it reaches a higher level than is present in the diet. In this way, concentrations will increase with passage along a food chain or ascent of a series of trophic levels.

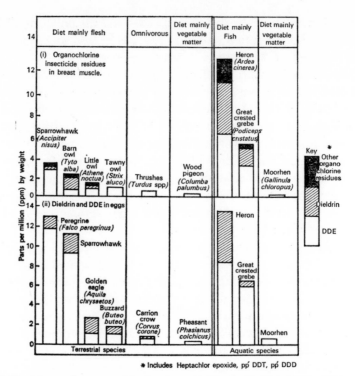

Fig. 5.3 Residues of organochlorine insecticides in British birds. See note (a)

1. Serrated Wrack, Oar Weed
2. Sea Urchin, Mussel, Limpet
3. Lobster, Shore Crab, Herring, Sand Eel
4. Cod, Whiting, Shag, Eider Duck, Herring Gull
5. Cormorant, Gannet, Grey Seal

(a) Trophic levels in Farne Island ecosystem

(b) Residue concentrations in relation to trophic level

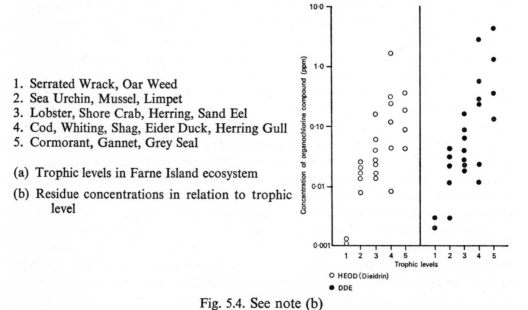

Fig. 5.4. See note (b)

64

The real situation is more complicated than this, however; one cannot assume that all of the absorbed chemical has originated from the diet, or that a predator removes a random sample of its prey population. These and other points are best illustrated by examples. Some time after Clear Lake, California, had been sprayed with DDD to control midges, the death of many western grebes provoked an intensive residue study of the ecosystem. At first glance the results, which are summarised in Table 5.5, appear to be a straightforward example of residue amplification along a food chain, but on closer inspection this is not the case. The concentration in lake water is given in terms of a bulk sample, whereas it is likely that much of this highly insoluble chemical was on the surface. In view of this it is debatable whether plankton accumulated a concentration of the chemical greater than that in its immediate environment. In the second place, fish are known to absorb fat soluble insecticides through the gills, so it is not clear how much of the residue burden in surface-feeding species is taken up this way, and how much comes from diet. Furthermore, the residues in the western grebe were determined in the body fat where they are bound to be several times higher than in the whole body. So did the birds really raise the concentration in their own bodies above that in the diet? These data do not give a clear answer. It is not certain that any of the steps in the food chain represent a true amplification of the concentration in the diet or in the ambient medium.

Table 5.5. DDD residues in Clear Lake, California

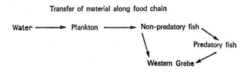

Transfer of material along food chain

Water ⟶ Plankton ⟶ Non-predatory fish ⟶ Predatory fish ⟶ Western Grebe

Residues found (ppm)

Item		
Lake water	whole sample	0·02
Plankton	whole sample	5·0
Non-predatory fish	fat	40–1000
Predatory fish	fat	80–2500
Predatory fish	flesh	1–200
Western grebe	fat	1600

Interpretation of residue data also raises the question of selective feeding. It cannot be assumed that the mean concentration in the diet of a predator is the same as the mean concentration in the prey population. The residues of dieldrin and heptachlor epoxide in grain-eating birds in Britain were found to be extremely variable and sometimes very high during 1959–61. At the same time it is well recognised that predatory birds are liable to select individuals that behave abnormally from the population upon which they prey. Indeed, birds of prey can be trapped by luring them on to tethered birds. It is distinctly possible that species like the sparrow hawk and peregrine falcon preyed upon severely poisoned grain-feeding birds rather than normal individuals at the time of the British seed-dressing incidents, i.e. their diet probably contained concentrations of dieldrin and heptachlor epoxide well above the average for the prey population.

Contrasting with this, levels of organochlorine compounds tend to be smaller and less variable in populations of marine fish than in seed-eating birds. In the case of the shag in the Farne Islands, average concentrations of DDE and dieldrin in whole carcasses were some fifty times higher than those in the sand eel which constitutes 96 per cent of its diet. Unless these residues were largely derived from some other source there must have been extremely efficient accumulation from the diet; DDE and dieldrin concentrations were not sufficiently variable in the sand eel to explain this observation on the basis of dietary selection.

So far, environmental residues of organochlorine insecticides have been discussed from the point of view of their distribution. It is now time to consider their effects upon individuals and populations.

Attempts to determine whether individual animals and birds have been killed by organochlorine compounds in the field depend upon making comparisons between the residues found in them and those present in the carcasses of poisoned experimental specimens, whilst taking note of any circumstantial evidence suggesting poisoning. Figure 5.5 presents some figures for residues of dieldrin found in animals, birds and fish collected in the field together with data for experimentally poisoned specimens.

The carcasses of buzzards and badgers were all found under circumstances suggesting dieldrin poisoning. Such was not the case with the kestrel, sparrow hawk and heron samples. It will be seen that the avian species dying in the field from suspected dieldrin poisoning contained lower average concentrations of the insecticide than the three species that were experimentally poisoned. Such factors as stress conditions and ingestion of other undetermined pesticides in the field may have contributed to this. Whatever the reason, these figures from the field and the laboratory taken together give some indication of a lethal concentration of dieldrin within a bird.

On the basis of this evidence, lethal concentrations in the liver are usually in the range 10–70 ppm. Interestingly, badgers from the field which were suspected victims of dieldrin poisoning contained between 16·9 and 46·3 ppm of the insecticide in the liver which falls in the middle of this range. Although a few of the kestrels, sparrow hawks and herons contained dieldrin residues of this order, the majority did not. Thus they were unlikely to have been poisoned by dieldrin alone.

Up to this point we have been dealing with the simple situation where the toxic action of only one compound is considered. However, residue analysis often reveals a number of different substances at detectable concentrations. Sometimes it is necessary to consider the joint action of several substances occurring in relatively small amounts. The trout and perch cited in Figure 5.5 were apparently victims of a complex pollution involving several different substances. Although dieldrin levels

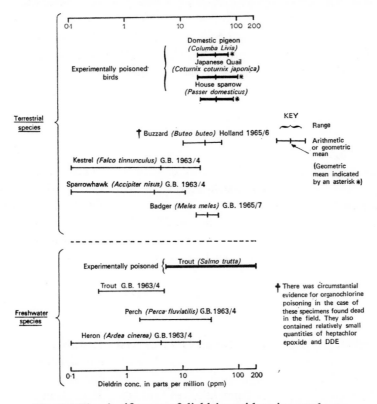

Fig. 5.5 The significance of dieldrin residues in vertebrate liver.
     Comparison between levels in specimens found dead in the field and those in experimentally poisoned specimens.

in the fish fall below those associated with lethal poisoning it is possible that this chemical was a contributory factor in causing their death. Some examples are given in Figure 5.5 of residues in British predatory birds found dead in the field during

1963–4. DDE, dieldrin, heptachlor epoxide, γBHC, ppDDT and DDD were all detected in certain of these samples. In the majority of cases concentrations of individual compounds were considerably below those known to cause death. Even if the effects of different compounds are assumed to be additive, it is unlikely that more than 10 per cent of the specimens died of organochlorine poisoning. Some of these species will be the subject of further discussion regarding effects upon populations.

The assessment of sub-lethal effects in the field also depends upon the use of data from controlled laboratory experiments. Once again a relationship is sought between a dose and an effect, and some examples are given in Table 5.6. The data for DDT and DDE illustrate a major difficulty with this sort of work. Several different sub-lethal effects on avian species have already been identified including delayed ovulation, alterations in the thyroid, thin egg shells and disturbances in calcium regulation and it is probable that many more await discovery. It is difficult to determine the significance of these diverse effects in the field.

Table 5.6. Sub-lethal effects of organochlorine compounds

Species	Dosing	Effect
1 Small Tortoiseshell butterfly (*Aglais urticae*)	10–200 mg/kg dieldrin applied to larvae	Increased number of deformed adults emerging from pupae
2 Rat	5 mg/kg/day of DDT	Increased irritability of central nervous system
3 Pheasant	500 ppm DDT in diet of female	Increased chick mortality
4 Pigeon (*Columba livia*)	9 mg/kg/day of pp DDT	Increase in size, and structural changes in thyroid
5 Japanese quail	100 ppm pp DDT in feed	Reduction in thickness and calcium content of egg shells
6 Mallard (*Anas platyrhyncha*)	10 ppm DDE in feed	Reduction in thickness of egg shells and hatchability of eggs
7 American sparrow hawk (*Falco sparverius*)	0·3 ppm dieldrin + 1·4 ppm DDT in feed	Reduction in egg shell thickness

Many of the observed effects are relatable to dosage rates of the chemicals and not levels in tissues, which makes it difficult to argue from available residue data. With the exception of examples 6 and 7 the effects reported here are at dosage rates considerably above those normally encountered in the field in Britain. However, they are not the lowest levels that will produce an effect and, as yet, 'no-effect' levels have not been determined. An important demonstration of sub-lethal effects by organochlorine insecticides comes from the work on the American sparrow hawk (*Falco sparverius*), a predator related to the peregrine falcon. Thin egg shells, an increased rate of egg breakage and reduced reproductive success attended the feeding of a diet containing 0·3 ppm of dieldrin and 1·4 ppm of DDT. This dietary level of dieldrin is lower than that encountered by grain-eating birds during the British seed-dressing incidents, whilst substantial quantities of DDT and its metabolites were found in eggs and liver samples from predatory birds after 1961.

Some sub-lethal effects of dieldrin are examples of latent toxicity. For example, the production of deformed adults in *Aglais urticae* is attributed to the action of dieldrin which is carried through to the pupal stage after dosing the larvae.

To summarise, some sub-lethal effects of dieldrin, DDE and DDT must have been produced in the field but their magnitude and importance remain a matter for speculation.

Whilst the foregoing findings are of interest to toxicologists, the question remains as to what effects these compounds are having on natural populations. Neglecting strictly local pollution problems, one important general effect of organochlorine insecticides has been claimed – a reduction in numbers of various predatory species in Europe and North America which has coincided with their widespread introduction into agriculture. The buzzard in Holland, the bald eagle (*Haliacetus leucocephalus*) in the U.S.A., the peregrine falcon and sparrow hawk in Britain and predatory invertebrates on agricultural land are all cases in point. The two British raptors have been extensively studied and will be discussed in more detail.

Both the sparrow hawk and the peregrine falcon experienced sharp population declines beginning in the mid-1950's and lasting into the early 1960's. These declines were coincident with the introduction of aldrin, dieldrin and heptachlor on a wide scale as seed dressings, were most pronounced in agricultural areas of Britain (Figures 5.6 and 5.7) and were followed by arrestment and recovery after the seed-dressing restrictions in 1961. Disappearance of the peregrine from southern England and the sparrow hawk from the highly agricultural eastern counties was almost complete. The declines were associated with diminished preproductive success and a high incidence of broken egg shells in nests.

Reference has already been made to residue surveys on these two predators after 1961 which showed that dieldrin, heptachlor epoxide and DDE were present in many specimens of carcasses or eggs (Figure 5.3). Since these figures post date the seed-dressing restrictions, and most specimens were not obtained from the agricultural areas where sharp declines had been experienced, the residues of dieldrin and heptachlor epoxide must be lower than those carried by birds in the affected

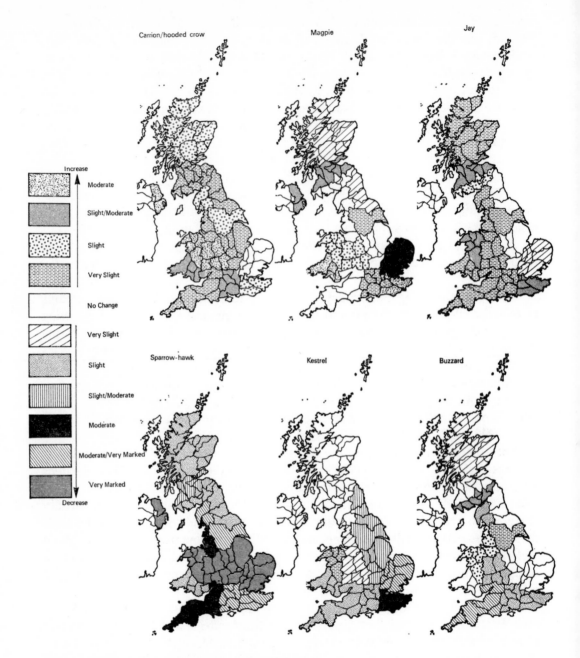

Fig. 5.6 Change in breeding status of British birds
Carrion/hooded crow, magpie, jay, sparrow, hawk, kestrel and buzzard
Estimated changes in numbers of breeding birds

Fig. 5.7 The peregrine falcon in 1961
The first figure represents percentage of territories occupied, the
second (in box) the percentage in which young were reared

areas during the period of population decline. Bearing in mind what has been said about dietary selection, it is estimated that the carcasses of 2–4 pigeons poisoned with dieldrin carry enough of the insecticide to kill a peregrine falcon, and similar arguments could be advanced for the sparrow hawk. Taking these two points together it is probable that both species suffered heavy mortalities as a result of ingesting dieldrin and/or heptachlor epoxide in their prey during the period in question. Arguing from toxicological studies (q.v.) it is also likely that thin egg shells and reduced reproductive success, events that were observed in the field, resulted at least in part from the residues of DDE and/or dieldrin in the birds at this time. Interestingly, examination of peregrine falcon and sparrow-hawk eggs from collections has shown that the shells became thinner during the period 1945–7 which coincides with the introduction of DDT on a large scale in agriculture. If this is a causal relationship it indicates that sub-lethal action of DDT or DDE did not initiate the decline of these species for this did not commence until some 10 years later; on the other hand, it could well have contributed to the decline once it had actually started. In conclusion, there is evidence that aldrin, dieldrin and heptachlor seed dressings were the main cause of the reduction in numbers of the two predators. Ingestion of a lethal dose from the prey is the most obvious mechanism, although sub-lethal effects were most probably in evidence as well, and their significance is hard to determine.

The finding of relatively high concentrations of DDE and dieldrin in predators

71

has raised questions about the levels in man, who is also at the end of a food chain. However, there are close controls over residues in food and analysis of samples of human body fat in Britain has shown that these compounds are at very much lower levels than are present in avian predators. There is no evidence that these low levels are of any significance. Since the voluntary restrictions on aldrin and dieldrin came into force in Britain, residues of dieldrin in human body fat have significantly declined, a trend that is likely to continue.

The effects of DDT and dieldrin on the soil fauna have also been studied; levels somewhat higher than those normally encountered in agricultural soils can cause a decrease in numbers of predatory mesostigmatic mites with associated increases of springtails (Collembola) upon which they prey. Millipedes, root-feeding aphids, and fly and beetle larvae can all fall in numbers following applications of DDT that give rise to concentrations of about 3 ppm in soil. It is not clear what the overall effects on soil fauna have been; any changes that have occurred should be reversed as the residues of organochlorine compounds in British soils decline.

At the time when aldrin, dieldrin, heptachlor and DDT were holding the stage in Great Britain and the U.S.A., another group of persistent compounds were receiving attention in Sweden. The organomercury fungicides have been in use as seed dressings and in wood processing since the 1920's but it is only within the last 20 years that evidence of harmful side effects in the environment has come to notice. It may seem curious that the problem has been taken more seriously in Sweden than elsewhere but this is partly a reflection of the particular organic mercury compounds that have been used there.

The early mercury fungicides were phenyl and alkoxyalkyl derivatives, but later on alkyl mercury derivatives also came into use (after 1940 in Sweden).

Table 5.7. Structure of organomercury fungicides

$CH_3Hg - X$	Methyl mercuric salts
$C_2H_5Hg - X$	Ethyl mercuric salts
$CH_3OCH_2 - CH_2Hg\ X$	Methoxy ethyl mercuric salts
$C_6H_5Hg - X$	Phenyl mercuric salts
$X =$ halide, acid, amide, phenol or thiol	

All together about one hundred different compounds have been used in commercial formulations based on the structure $R.HgX$, and the main types are detailed in Table 5.7. The properties of individual compounds are modified by the form of the group X, but certain generalisations can be made about the principal types. Nearly all are colourless solids with the alkyl compounds showing greater water solubility and volatility than aryl compounds possessing the same X grouping. Some show appreciable fat solubility.

There are important toxicological differences between the main groups of organo-mercury compounds. Phenyl and alkoxyalkyl mercury compounds are not very persistent in vertebrates and have biological half-lives of 3–4 days, which are similar to those for inorganic mercuric salts. Alkyl mercury compounds, on the other hand, are more stable and more slowly excreted, showing half-lives of 15 days in the rat, and 23–27 days in poultry. A disturbing feature of alkyl mercury compounds is their tendency to move into the brain (cf. lead tetra alkyls). They have lower LD_{50}s than phenyl or alkoxyalkyl derivatives, i.e. they are more toxic. In keeping with their marked persistence they show considerable chronic toxic action, and symptoms of poisoning in human beings may not appear until 3 to 4 weeks after dosing.

Both chronic and acute poisoning by alkyl mercury compounds is characterised by damage to the central nervous system which expresses itself in poor muscular co-ordination, loss of sense of position and impaired hearing. Certain typical symptoms of inorganic mercury poisoning such as kidney damage are usually absent. Organic mercury compounds can have sub-lethal effects upon birds including reduced reproductive success and behavioural changes.

Mercury compounds like those of other heavy metal ions can combine with sulphydryl groups and this may be the basis of their toxicity. Due to this interaction, it is hard to determine the state of mercury residues in animal tissues. Digestion of a tissue is usually necessary to release inorganic mercury for analysis, and this prevents identification of organomercurial residues.

Organomercury fungicides have two main uses in Sweden – for dressing seed and in the paper and pulp industry, and both practices are important sources of pollution. More than half of the entire Swedish cereal crop is dressed with them. When methyl mercury was in use it was estimated that 4·5 tons was added to soils per year. The pulp industry now releases about 3·5 tons of phenyl mercury per annum in effluents.

Much work has been done, especially in Sweden, to study the distribution of mercury in the environment. The whole subject is made difficult by the uncertainty of the source of mercury residues, the more so as no distinction has been made between organic and inorganic mercury in most vertebrate samples. Table 5.8 summarises some determinations of mercury residues in the Swedish environment.

Mercury poisoning has been quite common amongst seed-eating birds and their predators in Sweden, and in nearly all cases has been traceable to either methyl mercury dicyandiamide or ethyl mercury halide. Some results of residue surveys on wildlife are given in Figure 5.8. Recent work employing a new technique which distinguishes organic from inorganic mercury suggests that a considerable proportion of the mercury residues in wildlife specimens are in the organic form. This is supported by the relatively high levels of the element found in the brain in such

Table 5.8. Mercury levels in Swedish environment

Average mercury content of earth's crust	0·05 ppm
Moraine soils	0·13–0·25 ppm
Clay soils	0·08–0·15 ppm
Sandy and silty soils	0·05–0·35 ppm
Organic soils	0·30–0·51 ppm
Atmosphere	2 ng/m³
Rain water	0·2 ppm
Sea water	0·03 ppm
	(probably as $HgCl_2$)

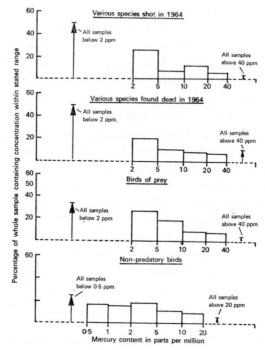

Fig. 5.8 Mercury residues in the livers of Swedish birds.

speciments. It will be seen that levels of mercury in the two top histograms range from 0–40 ppm in the majority of cases, with no sharp distinction between specimens that were found dead and those that were shot. There are, however, a higher proportion of specimens containing more than 20 ppm amongst those found dead and these may include a number of cases of lethal poisoning. Residue levels in predators are also high, but there is no clear cut distinction from concentrations in non-predators.

Organic mercury in effluents from pulping mills is an important source of river pollution. Concentrations as high as 5 ppm have been found in pike caught in such polluted waters. It has been found that levels in freshwater fish in Sweden are higher than those recorded in Germany, Norway, Switzerland and Japan in comparable surveys and that freshwater fish are more highly contaminated than marine fish. Some examples of levels in Swedish specimens are given in Table 5.9.

Table 5.9

Marine fish	Mackerel	0·06–0·08 ppm
	Herring	0·03–0·11 ppm
	Cod	0·15–0·19 ppm
Freshwater fish	Pike	5 ppm

Viewing the overall position, it is clear that environmental mercury levels are high in Sweden, relative to other countries, and that alkyl mercury compounds have been especially important as sources of the element. Furthermore, they have been responsible for bird mortalities in the field. However, attempts to relate population declines of certain predators, e.g. the white-tailed sea eagle, with organomercurials have been inconclusive and no serious fish kills have been attributable to them in spite of locally high concentrations in fresh water.

In Japan, human beings have died or suffered irreversible brain damage as a result of ingesting organic mercury in fish. The condition has been termed 'Minamata disease'. It appears that the organic mercury in this case was synthesised in the environment from inorganic mercury arising from industrial effluent. This tragic episode is one further example of the need to anticipate the transformation of pollutants after they enter the environment. Metabolites and products of chemical reaction can present different problems from the original pollutants from which they are derived.

So far, the organomercury fungicides and the organochlorine insecticides have been discussed separately. Indeed, they have been studied separately for the most part. However, they are frequently used together in seed dressings and often occur together in living organisms, e.g. in grain-eating species and their predators. This illustrates the point that organisms are often exposed to a variety of different pollutants in the natural environment, and to consider one compound or even one group of compounds may be to oversimplify the situation.

Biologically persistent 'nerve poisons' are represented in both groups, and the question arises as to whether there is any form of joint action between members of the two groups. There are grounds for suspicion since representatives of both groups have effects upon liver microsomal enzymes. Organochlorine compounds such as dieldrin and DDE can 'induce' these enzymes (q.v.). Methyl mercury compounds can have inhibitory effects upon some microsomal reactions at low concentrations, and this is apparently due to combination with sulphydryl groups. If the combined action of organomercurials and organochlorine compounds were to be additive or synergistic it would raise questions of interpretation. Birds poisoned by seed dressings, for example, could show unusually low levels of dieldrin or heptachlor epoxide due to the effect of organic mercury.

Although there is considerable disagreement over the ecological significance of residues of organochlorine insecticides and organomercury fungicides in the environment, the investigation of this problem has been very instructive. Information has been gained about the behaviour of persistent liposoluble poisons in the environment and this should provide useful guidance in the appraisal of future pollution problems.

VI

Detergents, Polycyclic Aromatic Hydrocarbons and Polychlorinated Biphenyls

T HESE three groups of organic pollutants contrast with one another in their physical and chemical properties, their origins and the manner of their release into the environment. These contrasts are to some extent reflected in their fate in the environment and in the problems that they present. Historically, the polycyclic aromatic carcinogens have existed as pollutants for very much longer than the other two groups because they are formed during the incomplete combustion of fuels. However, their chemical characterisation and identification in the environment are relatively recent events. On the other hand, detergents and polychlorinated biphenyls (PCBs) are products of modern technology and have only become a problem in the twentieth century. Members of all three groups have one feature in common – their presence in the environment has aroused the interest of public health authorities or conservationists or both.

Before synthetic detergents (syndets) came on to the market, most of their functions were fulfilled by ordinary soaps. Soaps have not caused serious pollution problems, for although they reach quite high concentrations in sewage, they are efficiently removed by bacterial oxidation and chemical reaction during passage through sewage beds. Such is not the case with syndets, many of which are only partially removed by sewage treatment. This is because they are not readily attacked by bacteria or brought out of solution by divalent cations. Ironically, resistance to precipitation is their great advantage over soaps with regard to cleansing properties.

All detergents are surface-active substances. They have both hydrophyilic (water-loving) and hydrophobic (water-hating) properties and fall into three groups: anionic detergents, cationic detergents and non-ionic detergents. Some examples are given in Figure 6.1. The first two groups owe their hydrophilic properties to

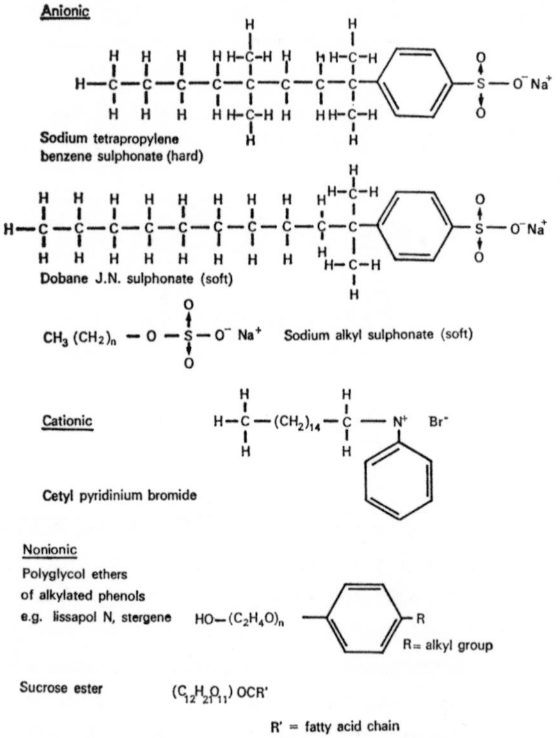

Fig. 6.1 Structure of synthetic detergents

charged groups, whereas non-ionic detergents do not – they merely have polar groups in the molecule which show affinity for water. The hydrophobic properties of detergents are due to long carbon chains and/or aromatic ring structures which show little polarity and no affinity for water.

Arising from their bimodal character, detergents are liable to arrange themselves on phase boundaries. In water, for example, they congregate at the surface with their non-polar parts pushing out into the air. This lowers the surface tension, so making air bubbles more stable and encouraging foaming. If non-polar organic material is present, the hydrophobic parts of detergent molecules become associated with it, leaving the hydrophilic groups in contact with water – another example of orientation to a phase boundary. In this way, fatty droplets and particles are stabilised as aqueous suspensions or emulsions, a property which is basic to the cleansing action of detergents and soaps.

Anionic detergents account for more than 90 per cent of total syndet usage in Britain at the present time, and, of these, akyl aryl sulphonates, such as alkyl benzene sulphonate, are the most important, being the active ingredients of familiar products such as Tide and Daz. Primary and secondary alkyl sulphonates, which are constituents of Dreft and Teepol, are less widely used than the foregoing. Non-ionic detergents represent only a few per cent of the present detergent production, whilst cationic detergents are even less important. The latter are too expensive for general use but are employed to a small extent in hotels and restaurants on account of their bactericidal properties.

The popularity of the alkyl benzene sulphonates as detergents is marred by their resistance to bacterial oxidation during sewage treatment. This has earned them the rather doubtful distinction of being termed 'hard' detergents, in contrast to 'soft' detergents such as most alkyl sulphonates which are more easily degraded. The consequence of this hardness is that more than half of the detergent arriving at a sewage plant can pass through unchanged. Foaming of sewage and diminished aeration of water are both consequences of persistence. As little as 1 ppm of an anionic detergent can reduce the rate of re-aeration by 20–30 per cent, and this causes a reduction in bacterial oxidation. Under these circumstances, lengthening of sewage beds is necessary if material is to be adequately treated before discharge. Some anionic detergents persist strongly in rivers and can be found many miles downstream from the sewage outfalls where they are released.

What are the practical consequences of the widespread use of hard detergents in terms of environmental pollution? Concentrations of up to 12 ppm of detergents have been reported in some American rivers, whilst in Britain levels ranging from 0·5 ppm to 5 ppm were recorded in a survey of eleven rivers. British rivers used for water supply, however, do not normally contain more than 0·5 ppm of detergent. Although these levels seem low they are still sufficient to limit oxygen uptake by rivers. Indeed, production of hydrogen sulphide in the Thames estuary was observed some years ago, and attributed to the anaerobic conditions caused by 1 ppm of detergent in the water. Another consequence of 1 ppm of detergent in river water is the development of masses of foam in rivers, aptly described as 'swans'. Foaming is not usually evident at outfalls but rather at weirs where aeration is strong.

Detergents can also have direct effects upon the fauna and flora of rivers. Anionic detergents are toxic to the water shrimp (*Gammarus palex*) at concentrations of 2·5 ppm or more over a period of seven days. Water fleas (*Daphnia spp*) and the pond weed (*Potamageton densus*) show a similar order of sensitivity. Fish are more sensitive to cationic and non-ionic detergents than to anionic detergents. For the species tested, anionic detergents have minimum lethal concentrations in water of 1–10 ppm. Although these levels are sometimes encountered in British rivers, their harmfulness is rather uncertain. The point is that rivers which intermittently contain concentrations of a few parts per million are usually heavily polluted with other things. Where this is so, they have a sparse flora and fauna, usually lacking species that are detergent-sensitive. Although this suggests that detergents are not having serious direct effects at the present time, the position could change if other forms of pollution were removed. Reduction of pollution by detergents should be an integral part of any scheme to clean up badly contaminated rivers.

Control of pollution has been approached in two distinct ways – more rigorous treatment of sewage and other effluents, and changes in the quantity and quality of detergents. One obstacle to progress has been the preference of housewives for hard detergents rather than soft detergents. Since 80 per cent of all detergent usage in Britain is domestic, this is a serious problem. Attempts are now being made to replace the currently popular substances with new soft detergents.

Hard alkyl benzene sulphonates owe much of their resistance to oxidation to the highly branched carbon chains in their structure which are not easily attacked by bacterial enzymes. A new soft detergent of this group is Dobane N. Sulphonate which has a simpler structure (Figure 6.1) than the foregoing compounds and is almost completely degraded during sewage processing. Other new compounds of this type are non-ionic esters of sucrose (Figure 6.1). If new substances of this kind replace the older hard detergents, then a solution to this pollution problem should not be far away. If may be added that certain hard detergents have already been banned in Germany, whilst there are signs that soft detergents are gaining ground in Britain.

In recent years, the problem of smoking and lung cancer has been given more publicity than the related question of environmental pollution by carcinogens, but this is not an accurate reflection of the amount of scientific activity in the field, for the subject of chemical carcinogenesis has been widely investigated and has inevitably led to a consideration of carcinogenic pollutants. As early as 1775, Sir Percival Pott reported a high incidence of scrotal cancer amongst chimney sweeps which he attributed to exposure to soot. Later investigations have confirmed his findings and it is now known that soot, smoke and other products of incomplete combustion of organic materials contain carcinogenic substances. Thus carcinogens of this type occur as environmental pollutants, notably in urban areas.

Coal tar is one source of these substances that has been intensively studied. It is rich in polycyclic aromatic compounds, some of which are carcinogenic. The most potent carcinogens in this group are composed of five or six fused benzene rings. The word 'potent' is used advisedly, for they have been shown to induce tumours in almost every tissue and animal species upon which they have been tested. They act at the site of application and the effective dose is of the order of micrograms. Two examples, 3,4 benzpyrene and 1,2,5,6 benzanthracene, are given in Figure 6.2.

3,4 benzpyrene has been quite widely investigated, is representative of the group, and will be used as a type example. It is found at levels of up to 1·5 per cent w/w in some coal tars, to which it imparts a characteristic fluorescence. Like other members

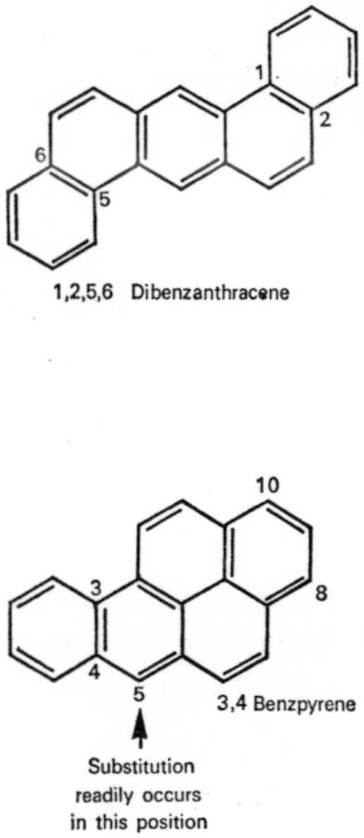

1,2,5,6 Dibenzanthracene

3,4 Benzpyrene

Substitution
readily occurs
in this position

Fig. 6.2 Polycyclic aromatic carcinogens

of this group, it is a solid of very low water solubility but shows some solubility in oils and other non-polar organic liquids. Unlike the general run of polycyclic aromatic hydrocarbons, it shows little tendency to undergo addition reactions but is very susceptible to substitution reactions in the 5 position (Figure 6.2). Interestingly, most other potent carcinogens in this group are also susceptible to substitution and it has been suggested that this is connected with their biological activity.

3,4 benzpyrene is attacked by microsomal oxidases with the formation of two hydroxy metabolites (Figure 6.3). These substances are also formed by living animals and are largely excreted as glucuronide conjugates. The two hydroxy metabolites do not display carcinogenic activity, so the metabolic transformations may be regarded as detoxifying. 1,2,5,6 dibenzanthracene is broken down in a very similar way, and the metabolites are again non-carcinogenic. 3,4 benzpyrene can induce a limited number of liver enzymes in comparison with organochlorine compounds such as

F

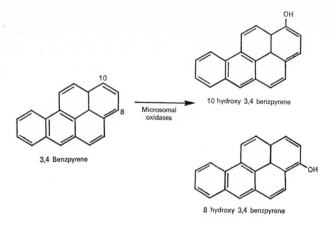

3,4 Benzpyrene

Microsomal oxidases

10 hydroxy 3,4 benzpyrene

8 hydroxy 3,4 benzpyrene

Fig. 6.3 Metabolism of 3,4 benzpyrene

DDT which are more general 'inducers'. Some workers regard this process as incipient carcinogenesis.

Surveys have shown that there is a correlation between air pollution and lung cancer and that there is a higher incidence of the disease in urban areas than in rural areas. Furthermore, this correlation can still be made after people have moved away from polluted areas. British immigrants in South Africa, for example, show a higher rate of lung cancer than the indigenous population although they do not smoke more heavily. Indeed, South Africans as a whole smoke more than the inhabitants of the British Isles yet have a much lower incidence of the disease.

These findings have raised questions about the carcinogenic action of air pollutants and attention has turned towards the polycyclic aromatic hydrocarbons. Some 40 aromatic hydrocarbons have been identified in polluted air, many of them polynuclear in character. A few are recognised carcinogens and these include 3,4 benzpyrene. Some values for levels of this compound in air samples and estimated intake by human beings are given in Table 6.1.

There is a tenfold difference between rural and urban air with respect to 3,4 benzpyrene content. Rural non-smokers inhale smaller quantities from the air than heavy smokers take in with cigarette smoke. There can be local variations in levels of polyaromatic hydrocarbons in town air. For example, air from the middle of a street in heavy traffic has been found to contain twice as much 3,4 benzpyrene as the general atmosphere.

Table 6.1. Levels of 3,4 Benzpyrene in air and estimated intake by humans

Place	Concentration in air mg/1000 m³	Intake per year with air in mg
N. Wales	5–6	41
Liverpool	62	450
London (in traffic)	1–68	7–475
Yearly intake by a heavy smoker (40 cigarettes per day)		120

In these figures there is a general correlation between incidence of lung cancer and inhalation of 3,4 benzpyrene either in tobacco smoke or in town air. The known carcinogenic properties of the compound support the idea that this is a causal relationship. On closer examination, however, this interpretation seems too simple. Transport workers have an occupational exposure to high levels of 3,4 benzpyrene and related compounds, yet they do not experience a correspondingly high incidence of lung cancer. Both polluted air and tobacco smoke are complex chemically, and it may be that lung cancer is caused by a number of different substances acting together rather than one single carcinogen.

When gas chromatography came to be used for the determination of organochlorine insecticide residues in specimens of wildlife, a series of related compounds were detected which defied identification for some time. At first it was thought that they might be breakdown products of these insecticides, but in 1966 Swedish workers showed that they were polychlorinated biphenyls (PCBs), a group of substances widely used in industry since the 1930's.

The correspondence between these compounds and the residues in wildlife specimens is strikingly illustrated by gas chromatography (Figure 6.4). Without going into details about the gas chromatographic method, it should be noted that each peak on a gas chromatogram usually corresponds to a single compound, although more than one compound sometimes contributes to one peak. A compound should always produce a peak in the same position on a chromatogram when using a particular set of operating conditions for the instrument. Thus the correspondence between the chromatograms shown in Figure 6.4 is powerful evidence for the presence of polychlorinated biphenyls in the extract from a wildlife specimen. Nearly all the peaks in the commercial mixture of polychlorinated biphenyls are also found in the tissue extract. Although one set of gas chromatograms do not provide conclusive identification, other analytical techniques substantiated the identification of polychlorinated biphenyls in this case.

Commercial products such as 'Aroclor' and 'Clophen A50' are complex mixtures

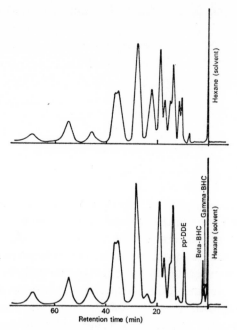

Fig. 6.4 Detection of polychlorinated biphenyls by gas chromatography

of polychlorinated biphenyls. The structure of the individual compounds has not been fully worked out, although they are known to be chlorinated derivatives of biphenyl

Chlorine atoms may be substituted in X-positions

It is known that the number of chlorine atoms per molecule varies between 5 and 8, but the substituted positions of the phenyl rings in the case of particular compounds have not been identified. Polychlorinated biphenyls are insoluble in water, but readily soluble in oils and many organic solvents. They do not conduct electricity and are stable to heat and most chemical reagents. In contrast to DDT and γBHC they are not dehydrochlorinated by sodium hydroxide.

There is growing evidence that polychlorinated biphenyls are widely distributed in the environment, especially in aquatic organisms. They have been found in fish and in a wide range of avian species in Europe and the U.S.A. Quantitative determination of them has presented difficulties, and many estimates of concentrations are only approximate. As with the organochlorine insecticides, they reach higher concentration in fat than in muscle, liver, brain and other tissues. In an extensive survey of avian species in the U.S.A., polychlorinated biphenyls were detected in all the specimens examined, but at lower concentrations than DDE. In Britain, relatively high residue levels have been found in freshwater fish-eating birds, predatory terrestrial birds (Figure 6.5) and in certain marine species such as the guillemot (*Uria aalge*) and kittiwake (*Rissa tridactyla*). In general these levels were below those found in experimentally poisoned Bengalese finches (Figure 6.5). Recently polychlorinated biphenyl residues of several hundred ppm were found in guillemots and other sea-birds washed up on the north-west coast of England. Some of these birds may have died as the result of poisoning by these compounds but it seems likely that other factors such as malnutrition, the stress of moulting and stormy weather contributed to this incident.

The polychlorinated biphenyls resemble the organochlorine insecticides in their physicochemical properties and in their distribution in the environment. Their presence in the environment poses similar problems for the toxicologist – too little is

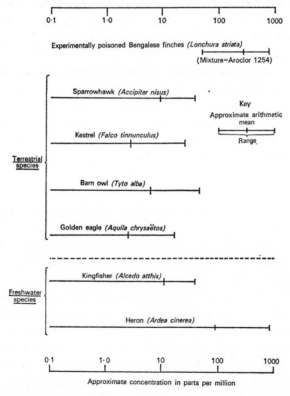

Fig. 6.5 Approximate polychlorinated biphenyl residue levels in livers of wild birds in Britain

known of their toxicity, and interpretation of residue levels found in wild specimens is difficult.

A number of physiological effects of polychlorinated biphenyls have been reported in vertebrates. Acne-like skin eruptions have been observed in men occupationally exposed to the compounds. Quail and domestic fowl show enlargement of the hydropericardium when dosed with high levels of them; this condition, however, has not been observed in wildlife casualties, so there is no evidence that it is important in the field.

Like certain organochlorine insecticides, polychlorinated biphenyls can induce liver enzymes. Pigeons yield liver microsomes showing a greatly enhanced capacity for metabolising the steroid oestradiol after dosing with 20 mg/kg 'Aroclor'. It has yet to be shown that this takes place in the field although it is distinctly possible in view of the fact that concentrations in excess of 20 ppm of polychlorinated biphenyls have been found in avian carcasses. Some workers have suggested that the thin egg shells produced by some predatory birds in recent years are the result of induction of liver enzymes by polychlorinated biphenyls and/or organochlorine insecticides. They argue that induction may disturb the balance of steroids that regulate calcium, and that this can lead to reduced deposition of the element during egg shell formation.

Another aspect of polychlorinated biphenyls which has yet to be investigated is their metabolic fate. The occurrence of a number of them in a wide variety of wild species suggests considerable biological persistence as one might expect from their fat solubility and chemical stability. There is evidence that the compounds with the smallest number of chlorine atoms to the molecule are the most readily metabolised. This has been demonstrated experimentally with the Japanese quail. Interestingly, field studies in the Rhine delta during 1965–8 showed that these less highly chlorinated compounds were more evident in fish than in sea-birds, perhaps indicating that they were too rapidly broken down to reach higher trophic levels in appreciable concentration. In view of the experience that has been gained with metabolites such as DDE and heptachlor epoxide, the metabolism of polychlorinated biphenyls calls for investigation. It is always possible that metabolites may be more persistent and/or more active than their parent compounds.

One unsolved mystery of this group of substances is how they get into the environment in the first place. Their industrial uses have not given any clear leads, for these are very widespread. They are used as plasticisers, lubricants, heat-transfer media and electrical insulators, and are incorporated into water-proofing compounds, putty asphaltic materials, printing inks, waxes and synthetic adhesives. One possible clue is the prevalence of polychlorinated biphenyls in organisms from marine and freshwater habitats. This may point to their release in industrial effluents, or from material dumped in the sea.

The similarities and differences between these three groups of organic substances may now be summarised. The detergents differ from the other two groups in that they are bimodal, showing affinity for both water and lipids. This is the reason for their surface-active properties, and is important in determining their distribution in surface waters. They decrease aeration of rivers and streams because of their ability to lower surface tension. One encouraging feature of detergents is that their biodegradability, and therefore their persistence, can be regulated by changes in molecular structure which do not cause any significant loss of their surface activity.

The polychlorinated biphenyls, on the other hand, are strongly non-polar and show no affinity for water. They are chemically stable and it appears that many of them are only slowly broken down by vertebrates. These points are reflected in the considerable levels found in a wide variety of carcasses from the field and the relatively high concentrations in body fat compared with other tissues.

Polycyclic aromatic carcinogens are also fat soluble but they are more chemically reactive than the polychlorinated biphenyls and are readily detoxified by microsomal oxidases. This does not suggest serious biological persistence. However, the point about these substances is that they are widespread atmospheric pollutants to which people are regularly exposed.

VII

Evaluation of Risks and Control
of Pollution

OFTEN the investigation of a problem throws up new questions instead of providing simple answers. The study of environmental pollution has been no exception, for much of the scientific effort has done little more than reveal our state of ignorance. Frequently, far more has been discovered about the distribution of chemicals than about their effects. Certain pollutants have been studied with success, leading to the formulation of some useful general principles, but no comprehensive statement can be made regarding the overall significance of pollution. Decisions on the control of pollution have had to be taken on limited evidence.

The greatest concern about pollution naturally centres upon man himself. In discussing this subject, occupational hazards are usually separated from the adverse effects of environmental chemicals, but the distinction is not always an easy one to make. The high mortality caused by the London smog is clearly a case of environmental pollution, but what view should be taken of the development of cancer by chimney sweeps or workers in factories handling asbestos? If seen in its widest sense, environmental pollution occurs in the factory and in the home. On the other hand, exposure of this kind is limited to specific premises and is largely a matter of individual choice. For this reason, it will not be discussed further here, where the point at issue is general pollution, and the special problems that it raises for governments and other public bodies.

There have been a number of cases where human beings have died as a result of environmental pollution. The deaths from hydrogen sulphide intoxication in Mexico, and the poisoning by alkyl mercury compounds reported in Japan, are examples of direct toxic effects. In other cases, pollutants have aggravated pre-existing disease conditions. The deaths caused by bronchitis during the London smog provide one example. There are also proven sub-lethal effects including the innocuous eye irritation caused by photochemical 'smog' and the serious brain damage resulting from alkyl mercury poisoning. Since many persistent pollutants are present in human beings there is reason to suspect that sub-lethal effects are commonplace, although they are difficult to establish unequivocally. At the same time this should not encourage an alarmist point of view, for although most drugs have sub-lethal effects these are usually mild and reversible. Until such effects by pollutants are character-ised, nothing can be assumed with regard to their significance.

The harmful effects of pollution are viewed somewhat differently when they are upon man as opposed to other animals. Whereas the fate of individual human beings causes general concern, it is only changes in whole populations that are of interest to conservationists.

In fact natural populations have been deliberately destroyed or limited by man-made chemicals, e.g. by the use of herbicides and insecticides on agricultural land. There are also many examples of unintended damage to wildlife. Some of the most clear-cut cases of this concern direct toxic action and have only affected limited areas. In 1957 some $2\frac{1}{2}$ million acres of land in the U.S.A. was sprayed aerially with 2 lb per acre of dieldrin or heptachlor to control the imported fire ant (*Solenopsis saevissima*). Subsequent applications were of heptachlor alone, at reduced rates. Severe losses of fish, wildlife, livestock and poultry followed these measures and some vertebrates completely disappeared from treated areas. A similar case, also in the U.S.A., was the decimation of avian species in woodland following the use of DDT to control Dutch elm disease. In many countries, certain rivers have been so seriously polluted that they have become almost totally devoid of life. Incidents such as these which clearly implicate particular pollutants have been well publicised and recognition of the problem has often led to its correction.

Other effects of pollution have been more insidious and less dramatic, but not necessarily less important. There is growing evidence that chemical pollutants have been the principal cause of the recent widespread decline of certain species, although it was not apparent at the time. Organochlorine insecticides have been implicated in some of these declines and their investigation has illustrated certain problems associated with persistent fat soluble pollutants. Pollutants such as DDE and dieldrin can become widely disseminated throughout the living environment largely as a result of transfer from organism to organism along food chains. Typically they are found at highest concentration in predatory species. Similar arguments have been advanced for other fat soluble substances such as alkyl mercury fungicides and polychlorinated biphenyls. There is evidence that organochlorine insecticides were important factors in the decline of the peregrine and sparrow hawk in Britain. Similar cases have been argued in Europe and the U.S.A., whilst in Sweden the reduction of some predatory species has been attributed to alkyl mercury fungicides (see Chapter V).

Since different species are in a state of dynamic equilibrium with one another in an ecosystem, the decline of one population is seldom without effect upon others. For this reason, a pollutant can cause changes in populations that are not directly affected by it. The decline of a parasite or predator can lead to the upsurge of a prey population. Some interesting examples of this concern the use of pesticides. In orchards the use of insecticidal sprays such as DDT has seriously reduced the natural predators of the red spider mite. This had led to a large increase in numbers of the mite which has thereby become a serious pest. Similarly, applications of DDT have caused increases in cabbage white caterpillars (*Pieris brassicae*) and collembola, apparently due to a reduction in numbers of parasites and/or predators. Again, use of herbicides has virtually eliminated many weed species from agricultural land with adverse effects upon the insect species that are dependent upon them.

A major stumbling block in the recent debate about ecological effects of pollution has been the paucity of information on the status of natural populations. In Britain, nation-wide surveys have been undertaken on various avian species including the peregrine falcon, the sparrow hawk, the kestrel, the magpie, the heron and the great crested grebe. This is a desirable line of approach, but it is much easier to operate in a small, densely populated island than in large, more thinly populated countries such as the U.S.S.R. and the U.S.A. In Britain, survey results have been mildly encouraging, for although the peregrine and the sparrow hawk have experienced sharp declines, most other species have not done so, and some have actually been increasing in recent years (Figure 5.6). Whatever effects pollutants may have had on these species, they have not caused any serious reduction in numbers. Perhaps this point is best illustrated by studies on the wood pigeon at the time of the British seed-dressing incidents. Although the species experienced heavy casualties due to poisoning by aldrin, dieldrin and heptachlor, there was no evidence of any long-term effect on its status. Indeed, it was estimated that more then 90 per cent of the population would have to be killed in one season to lower the numbers in the succeeding year. The important limiting factor was the food supply during the winter, which ensured that only a relatively small number of birds were able to survive into the next season. The relatively small percentage of the population killed by insecticides was more than accounted for by the normal winter mortality.

Looking to the future, it is to be hoped that population surveys will be continued and extended. To give one example there have been recent reports of heavy mortalities of sea-birds, some of them connected with oil slicks, others not adequately explained. The fate of these populations merits closer study linked to appropriate toxicological investigations.

Such factors as changes in food supply, habitat and climate can all cause population declines, and it can be extremely difficult to establish the role of pollutants. Similarly, it is not easy to prove that chemicals are having harmful effects upon human beings. The biochemical, physiological and toxicological aspects of this have been reviewed in Chapter II. One of the main problems at the present time is that so little is known of what pollutants actually do to living organisms in fundamental terms. LD_{50}s and LC_{50}s are only a crude guide to the risks associated with them. If the characteristic physiological and/or biochemical effects of particular substances were known, it would be easier to identify changes that they cause in the environment. Whilst there is undoubtedly room for improvement here, the sheer complexity of present-day pollution places severe limitations on the progress that can be made. The hope is that those aspects of the subject that receive close study will be wisely chosen.

So far the discussion has been limited to known effects of pollution and the prospect for assessing risks in the future. It is now time to review the steps that have been or can be taken to limit pollution. Much of the effective control to date has been dependant on the knowledge gained from hindsight. But prevention is better than cure, and in future it should be easier to anticipate problems before they arise. First of all, practical ways of controlling pollution will be considered, to be followed by a discussion of the aesthetic, legal and administrative issues involved.

Many pollution problems are directly related to the disposal of industrial and domestic wastes and can be solved by improvements in procedure if the cost can be met. The combustion of fuels releases smoke, grit, sulphur dioxide and carcinogenic hydrocarbons into the atmosphere. One of the easiest ways of controlling such pollution is by regulating the quality of fuel. Thus in smoke-free zones only smokeless fuels such as anthracite and coke may be burned. Similarly, the use of fuels low in sulphur limits the emission of sulphur dioxide. Considerable progress has also been made in purifying industrial flue gases. Sulphur dioxide can be removed by scrubbing with calcium bicarbonate solution, and grit by multi-cyclone dust separators and electrostatic precipitators. A practice that has recently been the subject of criticism is the use of tall chimneys to aid the dispersal of flue gases at a safe distance above ground level. Airborne pollutants released from high factory chimneys in England have apparently crossed the North Sea to Denmark, giving rise to 'fall-out' there.

Recently measures have been taken in California to control emissions from internal combustion engines. In the first place, improvements in engine design have been demanded to limit crank case emissions. Furthermore the use of exhaust after-burners has become necessary to control pollution by organic compounds and carbon monoxide. However, a serious difficulty has been encountered in one of the new types of after-burner. Lead derived from petrol anti-knocks is deposited in it, and impairs its function. It now seems likely that two problems will be solved instead of just one – lead-free petrol will have to be produced for use in cars fitted with this new exhaust attachment.

Many different techniques are employed in the treatment of trade wastes before they are discharged into rivers and oceans, and they will only be touched upon briefly here.

Often the best means of disposal of trade waste waters is through a local sewage works, if one is available in a convenient location that can cope with the discharge. Generally this provides a cheaper and better solution to the problem than does separate treatment of trade wastes in special plants.

A wide variety of physical and chemical processes are utilised for treatment of wastes, including sedimentation, filtration, dialysis, oxidation, reduction, precipitation and pH adjustment. Sometimes it is necessary to segregate different wastes from one industrial process so that they may be treated appropriately. Some potential pollutants are not released into waste waters – they are destroyed by combustion, or dumped into the oceans in stout containers. The last practice is not without its critics, who question how long such containers will remain intact.

Economic factors tend to determine the practices that are followed. If sufficient money were available, most disposal problems could be quickly resolved. Sometimes a potential pollutant has an economic value that offsets the cost of its removal from wastes. As certain natural resources diminish it is likely that more attention will be paid to this aspect of waste disposal.

Notwithstanding the use of some agricultural poisons domestically and industrially, these substances present different problems of control from the general run of pollutants. Their use in pest and weed control necessarily involves release into the environment, so control measures must be concerned with the way in which this is done, and what happens after release.

The impossibility of forecasting all effects in the field has already been stressed; nevertheless, there are a number of ways of improving the situation. In the first place, it is desirable to produce less persistent compounds. Sometimes this is in conflict with agricultural requirements, for persistence is necessary for the effective control of certain pests. For example, sheep farmers were reluctant to abandon dieldrin for ectoparasite control because the less persistent compounds that superseded it needed to be used more often to obtain satisfactory results. In spite of this, the last few years have seen the replacement of persistent organochlorine compounds by less persistent substances for a number of purposes. γBHC and the organophosphate insecticide, 'birlane', have largely replaced aldrin, dieldrin and heptachlor as seed dressings in Britain; organophosphate and carbamate insecticides are now often used instead of DDT for spraying various crops; alkyl mercury fungicides have been replaced by less persistent alkoxy and phenyl derivatives in Sweden.

Fundamental to this discussion is the question of where a chemical persists. Insecticides such as lindane and granular formulations of certain organophosphate compounds are quite persistent in soils, but their active ingredients are short-lived within animals. It is biological persistence that gives rise to most concern, and this raises the issue of selective toxicity which is relevant to drugs and food additives as well as to pesticides. Selective toxicity is desirable in any agricultural poison to ensure that pest organisms are more vulnerable than man, livestock, domestic animals and wildlife. Biological persistence is one factor influencing selective toxicity, for poisons can be more effective if their elimination is slow. Species that are well provided with detoxication systems for breaking down fat soluble poisons tend to be less vulnerable to them and are not liable to build up their concentrations within the body over long periods of time. Some important species differences have already been observed with regard to metabolic capacity. Fish, for example, show poor microsomal activity in comparison with most land vertebrates, and this may contribute to their marked tendency to accumulate organochlorine insecticides. In general, a better understanding of species differences with respect to metabolic capacity will make it easier to design more selective toxicants and avoid harmful side effects. It should also suggest new ways in which synergists may be used to further these ends.

Selective toxicity may be due to factors other than differences in metabolism. Differences in absorption, distribution or site of action may all be exploited to this end. However it is achieved, it furthers the objective of limiting undesirable side effects. Selective toxicity and limited biological persistence are both highly desirable features of any new pesticides.

There has been a tendency in the past to control pests with chemicals without paying much attention to the biological, ecological and climatological factors involved. Nowadays there is growing interest in the concept of 'integrated control', which attempts to see the exercise in terms of the whole environment, taking into account as many relevant factors as possible. The operation of integrated control should help to minimise the side effects of agricultural poisons, e.g. episodes such as the red spider mite epidemic should be more readily foreseeable if the relationships between pests and their natural parasites and predators are better understood. The use of biological rather than chemical control measures is part and parcel of the integrated approach, although it must be admitted that it has not been very successful up to the present time. The adoption of a more ecological approach to pest and weed control may call into question the economic value of certain practices. Already a survey on cereal crops in south-east England has indicated that the control of weeds by herbicides is having little effect upon yield, i.e. the competition of weeds is having no more harmful effect on the crop than the application of herbicide.

The successful application of scientific principles to pest control ultimately depends upon the co-operation of pesticide users. Just as housewives should be discouraged from using an extra squirt of hard detergent in the washing-up bowl, so agricultural and horticultural workers should be deterred from 'adding one for luck' when mixing their sprays. Approved agricultural products give details of the recommendations for safe use on their labels, but is this enough? Perhaps more needs to be done to make the public aware of the consequences of misuse.

Recommendations for the control of pollution are put forward on the basis of scientific investigation but whether they are implemented or not depends upon various legal, political, economic and social factors. Indeed, these very factors are important in determining what studies are undertaken in the first place.

Where committees or public bodies have to take decisions about control measures they often face the problem of quantifying the harmful effects of pollution. Sometimes this can be done by assessing cost, e.g. in terms of damage to buildings and lost working hours. If serious human health hazards are involved, assessment of cost is likely to be difficult, but is unimportant because the central issue is the welfare of man.

Decision taking is relatively simple where economic losses or severe hazards to human health are involved, but not if aesthetic considerations are paramount. There is no easy way of measuring the harmful effects of disfigured buildings, foul waterways or desecrated countryside upon human beings. Understandably, such issues do not often arise in underdeveloped countries. The importance of the spoiling of urban and rural landscapes pales into insignificance in the face of povetry, famine and disease. If a persistent insecticide is necessary to control the vector of a deadly disease or to raise agricultural productivity in a land visited by famine, little thought will be given to its side effects on wildlife.

On the other hand, the argument is different in more highly developed countries, where the issue revolves around the quality of life and economics rather than human survival. Here questions such as mental illness and the use of leisure in an industrial society become important. Britain, in common with other small and highly developed countries, has problems with overcrowded towns and increasing encroachment on the countryside. Some psychologists are concerned about the effects of overcrowded and badly planned towns upon people, effects that can be alleviated to some extent by access to unspoiled rural areas. The maintenance of areas of countryside for leisure is one of the main objectives of a conservation policy. The existence of two bodies – the Nature Conservancy and the National Trust – bears witness to the British commitment to conservation.

The control of pollution is an important part of such a conservation policy, and attempts are being made to assess the harmful effects of pollutants upon wildlife to further this aim. But as we have seen, the importance of these effects is largely an aesthetic question. Although most people would agree that there are unpleasant or unsightly consequences of pollution in the countryside, these are not usually measurable in terms of pounds and pence. Decision taking on conservation is often a rather subjective matter.

Public opinion can be very important in influencing decisions, and it in turn is conditioned by the views expressed by the mass media. This has its problems, for in presenting a complex situation to the public, oversimplification and consequent distortion are hard to avoid. Furthermore, mass media in general and newspapers in particular tend to be sensational. The consequence is that the public at large gets an unbalanced and rather misleading picture of a subject like pollution. That public opinion can influence decision taking in a society such as ours is of itself a desirable thing, but there is a real danger that unreliable information will precipitate unsound policy making. It has been suggested that the recent ban on cyclamates as sweetening agents is a case in point. Critics of the ban claim that the evidence against cyclamates was too flimsy, that the decision was unnecessarily alarmist and that it was only necessary to make appropriate labelling of relevant products compulsory. Be this as it may, it is doubtful whether the same decision would have been taken at a time when public opinion was less sensitive about polluting chemicals.

Most countries of the world have systems for controlling pollution. In the following account, the arrangements described will be those in operation in Britain unless otherwise stated. However, it should be borne in mind that pollution of the air and oceans can be an international problem that needs to be dealt with at international level.

The thirteenth-century law against burning coal in London lapsed in the sixteenth century and control of smoke emission was not reinstated until after the 1952 smog. The Clean Air Act came into force partially in 1956 and wholly in 1958. Until then legal action concerning atmospheric pollution by smoke depended upon establishing that a nuisance had been caused according to Common Law. This was not easy, and the 1956 act strengthened the law regarding smoke nuisance, and made it an offence to burn unauthorised fuels in Smoke Control Areas. Powers were given to local authorities to prosecute householders for not complying with the act. New furnace installation had to be inspected and approved by the local authority before coming into operation. Encouraging progress has been made since the act and Smoke Control Areas have been established in many parts of the country including certain towns such as Exeter and Oxford which were not heavily polluted at the time of the act.

Apart from smoke control, much has been done to limit the emission of noxious or offensive gases from commercial premises. The first Alkali Act of 1863 defined a number of trade processes requiring a certificate of operation. This had to be reviewed annually and was issued subject to the employment of the best practicable means to prevent pollution. Since then the Alkali (etc) Workers Regulation Act (1906) and the Alkali (etc) Works Orders (1928–63) have extended the scope of the law which now covers more than 3000 processes. The implementation of the law depends upon Alkali Inspectors who report annually to the Minister of Housing and Local Government, or to the Secretary of State for Scotland. They may be called in if a local authority claims that a registered establishment is contravening the act.

The photochemical 'smog' experienced in Los Angeles and other Californian urban areas was caused primarily by motor vehicle exhaust and led to far-reaching legislation designed to control air quality. To this end the State Department of Public Health has begun to define air levels of different pollutants associated with particular degrees of risk (Ambient Air Quality Standards). The levels are termed 'adverse', 'serious', and 'emergency'. 'Adverse' levels are those which merely cause undesirable symptoms or discomfort in human beings, or produce undesirable effects upon other organisms, buildings or the environment as a whole. In this category are concentrations of pollutants producing eye irritation, lowered visibility and damage to vegetation and buildings. 'Serious' levels are those likely to cause chronic disease or impairment of physiological function, whilst 'emergency' levels may lead to acute sickness or death. The last two categories apply to the most sensitive people in the community but not necessarily to the majority of the population. Although the impetus for this classification has come from photochemical pollution it also deals with other pollutants such as hydrogen sulphide and hydrogen fluoride. The standards for individual substances are not necessarily applicable to combinations of pollutants, physiological effects under unusual weather conditions or to pollutants occurring in aerosol form or in combination with aerosols. The definition of Ambient Air Quality Standards led to the development of Motor Vehicle Emission Standards to control release from exhaust and crank cases.

The Rivers (Prevention of Pollution) Act was introduced in 1951 with a view to strengthening the law as then laid down in the Rivers Pollution Prevention Act of 1876. The law applies only to England and Wales (Scotland and Northern Ireland have separate arrangements) and its enforcement is dependent upon 34 River Boards who now have powers formerly held by local authorities and a few special pollution bodies. Tidal waters are covered by a separate act – The Clean River (Estuaries and Tidal Waters) Act 1960. The act of 1951 makes it an offence to put any poisonous, noxious or polluting matter into a stream, subject to certain exceptions. Sewage effluents and trade effluents are acceptable if there is no practicable alternative manner of disposal, and if all reasonable steps have been taken to prevent the effluent from being unnecessarily poisonous or noxious. Another requirement of the act is that new discharges are not permitted without the consent of the appropriate River Board.

In addition to dealing with specific effluents, River Boards are increasingly involved in the assessment of water quality. Regular monotoring schemes are employed to measure such things as pH, biological oxygen demand (B.O.D.), suspended solids and pesticides in river water. As part of this work, individual River Boards define standards for various pollutants in trade and sewage effluents. Special responsibility for carrying out research on purification of effluents and effects of river pollution is borne by the Water Pollution Research Laboratory which is financed partly by the government, partly by industry.

Although much remains to be done, significant advances have been made in the reduction of river pollution over the last few years. This is the result not merely of tighter legislation but also of effective co-operation between local authorities, industry, and River Boards.

Marine pollution is very much an international problem, and has been investigated by the Inter-Governmental Marine Consultative Organisation (I.M.C.O.), in collaboration with the United Nations Educational, Scientific and Cultural Organisation (UNESCO) and other bodies. One outcome of international collaboration in this field has been an International Convention for the prevention of pollution of the sea by oil, originally formulated in 1954 and amended in 1962. This is designed to control the discharge of oily wastes during the normal operation of ships. It is likely that a further amendment will be adopted to prohibit all discharges subject to certain exemptions. This Convention has not been an easy one to enforce – some of the difficulties became evident during the recent *Torrey Canyon* incident. Fundamental to the successful operation of this and other schemes for controlling marine pollution is effective collaboration between governments, and full co-operation from the masters of ships.

Agricultural poisons present special problems with regard to control. The Agriculture (Poisonous Substances) Act of 1952 is designed to protect users of toxic chemicals. Substances which are dangerous to apply are classified into three groups according to the protective clothing that users are required to wear. The marketing of agricultural chemicals is controlled by two voluntary schemes. The Pesticides Safety Precautions Scheme depends upon the submission of relevant data by the manufacturers of a product. They agree not to market the product until the data have been examined under the scheme, and recommendations for its safe use have been made. Once this has happened, the product can be approved under the Agricultural Chemicals Approvals Scheme if it fulfils the claims made on the label. The label bears a summary of the recommendations of the Pesticides Safety Precaution Scheme, and the insignia of the Approvals Scheme.

The Advisory Committee and its scientific sub-committee are made up of representatives from such organisations as the Ministry of Agriculture, the Agricultural Research Council, the Natural Environment Research Council, the Laboratory of the Government Chemist, the Medical Research Council and the universities. They seek data on physical, chemical and biological properties of compounds, their persistence, breakdown, mode of action and toxicity. Thus their recommendations can be based upon very broad considerations including hazards to consumers, farm animals and wildlife.

Approved uses of agricultural chemicals are subject to revision in the light of new information and advice; for example, the Advisory Committee of the Pesticides Safety Precautions Scheme recommended major restrictions in the use of aldrin and dieldrin in 1964, and these were accepted. Further limitations of organochlorine insecticides were arranged in 1969.

There are already indications that these measures have had some effect. Dieldrin levels in human body fat in south-east England have fallen by about half since 1964, whilst there has been some recovery of peregrine and sparrow hawk populations during the same period which may be connected with declining dieldrin residues in the environment.

Generally speaking, the machinery for controlling pollution is well developed in Britain and is reasonably supported by law. One possible line of improvement is the development of comprehensive quality standards for air, water and food. These could aid the identification and control of pollutions arising from diverse sources – a point that is being demonstrated in California today. Tackling the problem in this more comprehensive way should improve collaboration between interested parties and aid the pooling of ideas and resources – in the past the effort has been rather fragmented. The interests of the Natural Environment Research Council are wide-ranging and include many aspects of pollution. There is the opportunity for a broad-fronted approach here if the funds are forthcoming to support it.

The recent wave of publicity about chemical pollution has been accompanied by increasing activity on the part of scientists, administrators and politicians, especially in the more affluent countries, and there is good reason to suppose that understanding of the effects of pollutants will improve over the next few years. But this is not saying much because the complexity of the situation will permit only a very limited understanding. On the optimistic side, it must be said that there is no evidence as yet of any disastrous effects upon man or indeed upon the great majority of natural populations that can be attributed to pollution. At the same time, some forms of pollution are increasing. This is true of pollutants released from the internal combustion engine, for example. With the rapid development of chemical industry new potential pollutants will be produced in the future. Thus there are no grounds for complacency – the situation must be kept under close surveillance.

It has already been stressed that many of our recognised pollution problems can easily be solved if sufficient money is available for the purpose. Indeed, a great deal of progress has already been made by improving the disposal of effluents, cleaning up flue gases, using more selective and less persistent pesticides and by more thoroughly informing users of potential pollutants. However, prevention is better than cure, and it is always important to consider whether pollution is the result of practices that are of value to the community.

Sometimes pollution is the inevitable outcome of a particular practice. Where the practice is of social importance, such 'unavoidable' pollution may be justified in the eyes of the community as in the case of DDT pollution arising from its use in malaria control. On the other hand, it is very hard to justify some forms of 'unavoidable' pollution because the social benefits are small or non-existent. Sometimes cases like this involve a vested interest which is in conflict with the interests of the community.

It is important that the risks associated with such 'unavoidable' pollution are seen in relation to the benefits that they bring to the community. Society has a right to decide whether it is prepared to be put at risk by particular practices; in the extreme case there is no reason why Society should accept risks resulting from practices from which it derives no overall benefit.

Further Reading

MELLANBY, K., *Pesticides and Pollution*, Collins (1967). An accurate and readable account of pollution in Great Britain.

Report of the Air Conservation Commission of the American Association for the Advancement of Science (1965), *Air Conservation*.

Deals with the main types of air pollution and discusses the question of air-quality standards.

KLEIN, L., *River Pollution*, **I**, **II** and **III**, Butterworth (1959, 1962, 1966).

A very detailed account of various aspects of river pollution.

GOODMAN, G. T., EDWARDS, R. W. and LAMBERT, J. M. (Editors), *Ecology of the Industrial Society*. A symposium of the British Ecological Society (1964).

Contains a number of separate articles on different aspects of the pollution problem in Great Britain including organochlorine insecticides, heavy metals, air and water pollution, and pesticide residues in soils.

EDWARDS, C. A., *Residue Reviews*, **13**, pp. 83–132, Springer Verlag (1966).

A clear and concise account of the problem of insecticide residues in soils.

HYNES, H. B. N., *Biology of Polluted Waters*, Liverpool University Press (1960).

A readable account of water pollution.

MOORE, N. W. (Editor), *Pesticides in the Environment and their Effects on Wild Life*, *Journal of Applied Ecology* 3, Supplement, Blackwell (1966).

Contains a number of articles on persistent insecticides in the environment, and their toxicological, physiological and behavioural effects.

BLOOD, F. (Editor), *Essays in Toxicology*, **1**, pp. 116–51, Academic Press (1969). *Lead Poisoning—An old Problem with a New Dimension.*

PARKE, D. V., *Biochemistry of Foreign Compounds*, Pergamon Press (1968).

Gives an account of the metabolism, absorption, distribution and excretion of foreign compounds, and gives details of the metabolic conversions of various drugs and economic poisons.

American Chemical Society, *Advances in Chemistry Series*, no. **60**, *Organic Pesticides in the Environment* (1966).

Contains a great deal of information on pesticides in the gross environment.

O'BRIEN, R. D., *Insecticides: Mode of Action and Metabolism*, Academic Press (1967).

Describes the metabolism and what is known of the mode of action for most of the common insecticides.

BRINCK, P., *The Mercury problem*, Oikos, Acta-Oecologica Scandinavica, Supplement 9, Munksgard, Copenhagen (1967).
Various authors deal with different aspects of mercury pollution with particular reference to Sweden.

CLAR, E., *Polycyclic hydrocarbons*, Vol. 1., pp. 133–60, Academic Press/Springer Verlag (1964).
Discusses the action of polycyclic aromatic carcinogens.

PRESTT, I., JEFFERIES, D. J. and MOORE, N. W., *Environmental Pollution 1*, **3** (1970). *Polychlorinated Biphenyls in Wild Birds*.
A recent account of one aspect of PCB pollution in Great Britain.

Advisory Committee on Pesticides and Other Toxic Chemicals, *Further Review of Certain Persistent Organochlorine Pesticides in Great Britain*, H.M.S.O. (1969).
A recent report on persistent pesticides by a committee with an important function in the Pesticides Safety Precaution Scheme.

RUDD, R. L., *Pesticides and the Living Landscape*, Faber & Faber (1965).
An ecological view of pollution by pesticides with particular reference to the position in the U.S.A.

Glossary

adaptive enzyme – A bacterial enzyme that is developed in response to environmental change

3,4 benzpyrene – A polycyclic aromatic hydrocarbon that is powerfully carcinogenic

γBHC – Benzene hexachloride. The γ isomer (lindane) is used as an insecticide

carbamates – Derivatives of carbamic acid, some of which are insecticidal

cerebrospinal fluid – Fluid contained in the sub-arachnoid space which surrounds the central nervous system

2,4D – 2,4 dichlorophenoxy acetic acid – a plant growth regulator herbicide

DDD – An organochlorine insecticide related to DDT. The technical material contains mainly the *pṗ* isomer

DDE (pṗ DDE) – Stable, persistent metabolite of *pṗ* DDT

DDT – Organochlorine insecticide. Main insecticidal component is *pṗ* DDT

dieldrin – Organochlorine insecticide – refers in this account to H.E.O.D., the main component of the insecticide

ecology – The study of the interaction of organisms with their environment and with one another

endogenous compounds – Compounds produced within a particular organism

endosulfan – An organochlorine insecticide

exogenous compounds – Compounds originating outside a particular organism

forensic science – Science applied to legal problems, e.g. murder cases, accidents, etc.

free radical – An uncharged fragment of a molecule with a free electron that is normally highly reactive

heptachlor epoxide – Stable metabolite of heptachlor, an organochlorine insecticide

hexabarbitone – A barbiturate drug

hyperthyroidism – Enlargement of the thyroid

induction – Refers here to an increase of enzyme activity, usually due to synthesis of new protein

lead tetra alkyls – Organic lead compounds used as anti-knocks in petrol

MCPA – 2,4 methyl chlorophenoxyacetic acid – a plant growth regulator herbicide

mμ – Millimicron – a unit of length, 10^{-6} mm

ng – Nanogram, a unit of weight, 10^{-9} g

paraquat – A bipyridilium herbicide which has only short-term activity in the soil.

polar – A molecule showing unequal distribution of electrons, i.e. showing electropositivity and electronegativity *polychlorinated biphenyls* – A group of chlorinated compounds used in commercial mixtures for insulation, plasticising, etc.

polycyclic aromatic hydrocarbons – Compounds consisting of two or more fused aromatic rings

ppm – Parts per million

synergism – The substantially more than additive toxic or pharmological action of two substances applied together

T.E.P.P. – Tetraethyl pyrophosphate – a highly toxic organophosphate insecticide

triazines – Heterocyclic nitrogen compounds, some of which are used as herbicides

trypanocidal – Controls trypanosomes – protozoa causing sleeping sickness in certain vertebrates including man

μ – Micron – a unit of length, 10^{-3} mm

μg – Microgram – a unit of weight, 10^{-6} g

Index